RED LEVEL

SPELL IT OUT

READING AND SPELLING PRACTICE

GLOBE FEARON
Pearson Learning Group

D1377222

RED LEVEL

SPELL IT OUT

READING AND SPELLING PRACTICE

Phillip K. Trocki

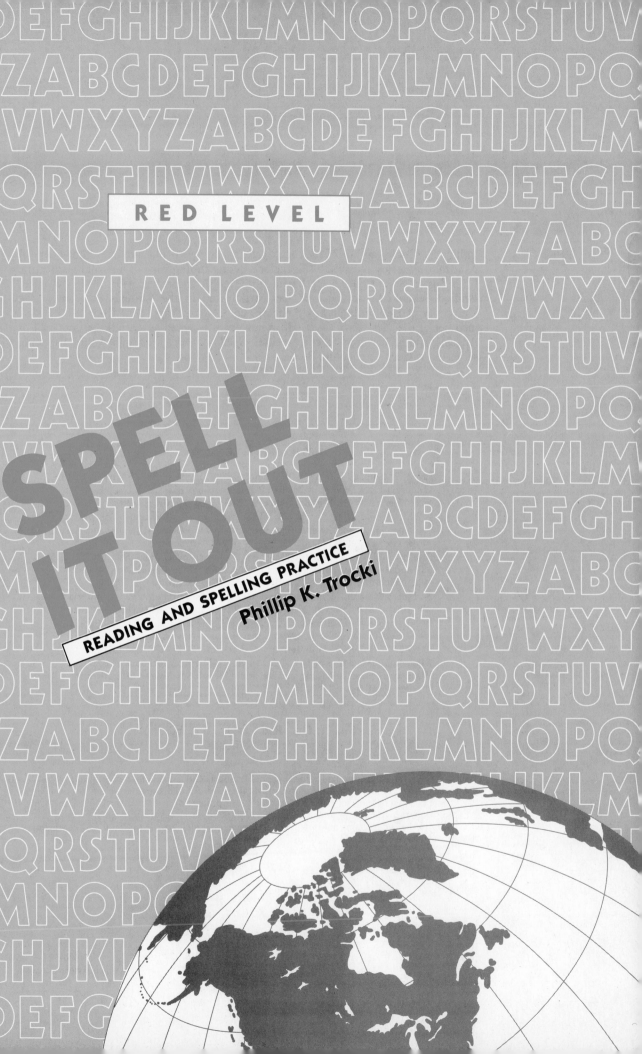

THE AUTHOR

Phillip K. Trocki, author of the four *Spell It Out* workbooks and co-author of the *A Need to Read* series, received his bachelor's degree in English and secondary education from Boston State College. He has taught English and reading for the Los Angeles Unified School District, and he has participated in the Writer's Program at the University of California at Los Angeles. For several years, Mr. Trocki was a staff member of the *New York Times*. He is currently assigned as a studio teacher in Los Angeles, and he has most recently written *Spelling Workout,* an eight-volume spelling series for Modern Curriculum Press.

PHOTO ACKNOWLEDGMENTS

Page 1, 2: Gamma Liaison; 4: NBC Photo; 9, 10, 12: Jerry LaFavor/Skytypers Inc.; 17: National Park Service; 18: Michael P. Johnson/photo, Base Camp, equipment; 20: Mike Hoover; 25: US Fish & Wildlife Service/J. Malcolm Greany; 26: US Fish & Wildlife Service/Ralph Touen; 28: Ministry of Tourism/Government of British Columbia; 33, 34, 36: National High School Rodeo; 41: Michael P. Johnson; 42: Rex Weyler/Greenpeace; 44, 73, 81, 89, 90, 92, 106: H. Armstrong Roberts; 49, 50, 52: Seaquest Int'l Inc.; 57: Woodfin Camp; 58: Photo courtesy of Movie Star News; 60: Bill Auth/Georgetown University Archives; 65, 68: Philip Galgiani/San Francisco Museum of Modern Art; 66: Mary McNally/San Francisco Museum of Modern Art; 74: Binney & Smith; 76: Rhoda Sidney; 82, 84: The University Museum: University of Pennsylvania; 97, 98, 100: Maren Seidler; 105: State of Maine Development Office; 108: Maine Dept. of Commerce & Industry; 113, 116: AP/Wide World Photos; 121, 124: Taurus Photos/E. Kroll; 122: Michael Halsband; 129: Allstate Life Insurance; 130, 132: Epilepsy Foundation of America; 137, 138, 140: Franklin Williamson/Zoological Society of Philadelphia; 145, 148: Aerovironment Inc.; 146: Miami Metro Dept. of Publicity and Tourism; 153, 154: Smithsonian Institution; 156: Philadelphia Museum of Art.

Spell It Out, Red Level, Third Edition
Phillip K. Trocki

ISBN: 1-55675-351-9
Printed in the United States of America

13 14 15 16 17 18 19 20   06 05 04 03 02

1-800-321-3106
www.pearsonlearning.com

TO THE STUDENT

Spell It Out, Red Level is designed to give you practice in reading and spelling. Both are skills you need to communicate with other people.

Each unit is divided into two parts. First, in Developing Reading Skills, you will find a short story about an interesting topic or personality. Some subjects you may already know about. Others may be totally new to you. In any case, read the story, paying attention to the details and the point the author is trying to make. Then answer the questions that follow without looking back to the story for help.

The second half of the unit deals with Developing Spelling Skills. The words you will be working with are ones that you use every day. In fact, many of the examples have been taken from the story that you just read. A few rules of spelling will be explained in the lessons. There are, unfortunately, exceptions to the rules. Some words will have to be memorized. Try to memorize them before you begin the exercises. That way, you will have more practice writing the words correctly. If you do spell a word wrong, don't be discouraged. Some words are harder to spell than others. Just try to find out what it is about the word that makes it hard to spell. Keep that in mind when writing the word again.

Above all, enjoy yourself when using this book—that's what learning is all about!

CONTENTS

Here's Jay

"To get paid for this is amazing. It's very silly." That's what Jay Leno has to say about his success. But that's just what Jay gets paid for. As a comedian he points out the silliness in the world.

At six feet tall and 180 pounds, Jay is a big guy among the other funny guys. At one point in his early career, an agent asked him to become a wrestler! "I don't want to wrestle." Jay told him. "I'm a comedian." "So you could be a funny wrestler," the man said. "You could fight and tell jokes. Say 'Grrrrr.'"

"I come from the kind of family where my mother ironed my socks." Jay says. "If my shoe ever fell off, people would know I came from a good family."

Jay's comic antics started early in life. "I was never good at spelling or adding, but I always could remember what made people laugh." Apparently, his teachers agreed. His fifth grade report card read: "If Jay spent as much time studying as he does trying to be a comedian, he'd be a great student."

Comedy did help pay for his college education. Jay made money as a stand-up comic. It wasn't easy getting jobs. Sometimes, he would give the manager of a club a fifty-dollar deposit on his act. He'd say, "Just let me tell some jokes. If people leave, you keep the fifty." "Most people were pretty nice," Jay says. "Even if they didn't like me, they'd give the money back."

In his free time, Jay likes to collect cars and motorcycles. He owns over twenty motorcycles. In fact, his real dream is to "go to mechanics' school." He has friends who are mechanics. When he tells them what he does for a living they say, "Gee, that's too bad." Jay says, "After this comedy stuff ends, I'm going to begin my real career, as a mechanic."

He figures he can keep the funny business going until he's 70. "I just want to keep doing what I'm supposed to do. And as long as people continue to show up...I'm happy."

REVIEWING YOUR READING

Circle the letter beside the word or phrase that best completes the sentence.

1. Physically, Jay Leno is

   a. a very small person.
   b. over 250 pounds.
   c. shorter than most comedians.
   d. a big person.

2. An agent once asked Jay Leno to become

   a. a mechanic.
   b. a singer.
   c. a wrestler.
   d. a writer.

3. Jay says that he was never good at

   a. adding and spelling.
   b. reading.
   c. physical education.
   d. making people laugh.

4. Jay worked as a comedian

   a. while he was in high school.
   b. while attending college.
   c. during grade school.
   d. during summer vacations.

5. Sometimes Jay would

   a. put a deposit down on his act.
   b. sell jokes to other comedians.
   c. pay people for listening to his jokes.
   d. buy jokes from other comics.

6. In his free time Jay likes to collect

   a. cars and bicycles.
   b. comedy films.
   c. motorcycles and cars.
   d. trucks and motorcycles.

7. You can conclude that Jay

   a. wanted to be a comedian when he was younger.
   b. studied very hard in school.
   c. came from a family of comedians.
   d. wanted to become a wrestler.

8. You can conclude that someday Jay would like to

   a. open a motorcycle store.
   b. learn more about mechanics.
   c. teach auto mechanics.
   d. go back to college.

FIGURING THE FACTS

Decide whether the following statements are true or false. Write _T_ on the line if the statement is true. Write _F_ if the statement is false.

1. Jay Leno thinks that getting paid for comedy is amazing. _____

2. Leno often points out the silliness in the world. _____

3. Jay's mother always wanted him to become a funny wrestler. _____

4. Jay says that his mother used to iron his socks. _____

5. Jay's teachers thought he was a good student. _____

6. Jay could always remember what made people laugh. _____

7. Getting jobs as a comic was always easy for Jay. _____

8. He owns over 20 motorcycles. _____

9. Jay plans to keep working until he is 70. _____

10. Jay's real dream is to teach comedy. _____

WHAT'S YOUR OPINION?

1. Do you think that putting a fifty-dollar deposit on his jokes was a good thing for Jay to do or a bad thing? Why?

_____

_____

_____

_____

_____

_____

2. What do you think Jay means when he says, "I just want to keep doing what I'm supposed to do"?

_____

_____

_____

_____

_____

_____

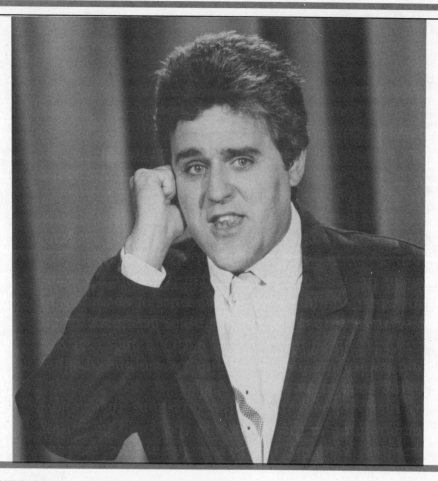

DEVELOPING SPELLING SKILLS

Study List

activities
apologies
authorities
classifed
copied
defying
envying
injuries
magnifying
multiplying
occupied
relying
satisfied
studies
supplied
theories

The following words contain a final *y* that is preceded by a consonant.

injury   occupy   study   rely

Notice that when we add a suffix to these words, the *y* is changed to *i* except when adding *ing*.

injuries   occupied   studies   relying

Rule: **When a word ends in *y* preceded by a consonant, change the *y* to *i* before adding any suffix except *ing*.**

As you can see, this rule applies when changing words to the plural as well as when adding other suffixes.

On your left is a Study List of words. Each has been formed by adding a suffix to a word that ends in *y* preceded by a consonant.

SKILL DRILL 1

Add the suffix to the word that ends in *y* to form words from the Study List. Remember the *y* to *i* rule. Write your answers on the lines provided.

1. injury + es = _____

2. multiply + ing = _____

3. apology + es = _____

4. satisfy + ed = _____

5. classify + ed = _____

6. supply + ed = _____

7. copy + ed = _____

8. magnify + ing = _____

9. occupy + ed = _____

10. rely + ing = _____

11. authority + es = _____

12. study + es = _____

13. theory + es = _____

14. defy + ing = _____

15. envy + ing = _____

SKILL DRILL 2

The following are short definitions of words from the Study List. Fill the blanks with words from the Study List that match the definitions. If you need help, check the Mini-Dictionary in the back of this book.

1. Being jealous of another's good fortune   _____

2. Officials of the government   _____

3. Damages from harms, or hurts   _____

4. Depending on or trusting   _____

5. Words of pardon for an offense or accident   _____

6. Taken up, filled, or lived in   _____

7. Increasing in number or amount   _____

8. Resisting or challenging authority   _____

9. Having made a copy of something   _____

10. Making something look bigger than it really is   _____

11. Contented or fulfilled   _____

12. Explanations of why or how something happens   _____

13. Lessons or school subjects   _____

14. Arranged in classes or groups   _____

15. Having satisfied a need or provided a quantity of something   _____

SKILL DRILL 3

Complete each sentence by adding a suffix to the word in parentheses to form a Study List word.

1. The children left the table completely (satisfy) _____ .

2. Tim and Louise expressed their (apology) _____ for the accident.

3. Prisons are full of people who have spent their lives (defy) _____ the law.

4. The books should be (classify) _____ according to title.

5. Please spend at least two hours on your (study) _____ tonight.

6. Scientists have several (theory) _____ about the disappearance of the dinosours.

7. There is a small (magnify) _____ glass on the shelf.

8. Agnes (copy) _____ the paragraph word for word.

9. We will be (rely) _____ on the brook for our water supply.

10. Many players suffer (injury) _____ while on the court.

11. Please report any problems to the proper (authority)_____ .

12. (Envy) _____ the success of others is a waste of time.

13. Mrs. Anderson (supply) _____ all the students with pencils.

14. The number of weeds in the garden is (multiply) _____ rapidly.

15. The brown house at the end of the street is (occupy) _____ .

SKILL DRILL 4

Answer the following questions by using words from the Study List.

Which words end with the suffix *ing*?

1. _____   3. _____

2. _____   4. _____

5. _____

Which words appear in their plural form?

6. _____   7. _____

8. _____   9. _____

10. _____

Which words end with the suffix *ed*?

11. _____   12. _____

13. _____   14. _____

15. _____

WORD GAME 1

This is a crossword puzzle without clues! Study the length and spelling of each word in the Study List. Then figure out which words fit in the spaces.

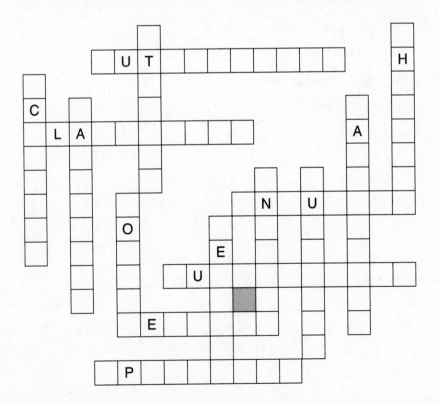

Study List

apologies
authorities
classified
copied
defying
envying
injuries
magnifying
multiplying
occupies
relying
satisfied
studies
supplied
theories

HOW WELL CAN YOU SPELL?

Try to take this practice test without looking back at Lesson 1. After you have finished, check your work against the Study List. Correct any mistakes you have made.

A. One word in each of the following pairs of words is spelled incorrectly. Circle that word and spell it correctly on the line provided.

1. satisfyed, studies   _____

2. activities, enving   _____

3. magnifing, copied   _____

4. classified, defing   _____

5. occupied, apologyies   _____

6. supplyed, relying   _____

7. multiplying, authoritys   _____

8. injuryes, theories   _____

B. In each of the following sentences, one word is spelled incorrectly. Find that word. Then spell it correctly on the line provided.

9. The fire victims are reling on the government for
   support.   _____

10. Club members are classifyed according to their age.   _____

11. Einstein was the author of many scientific theorys.   _____

12. George will return to his studyes next week.   _____

13. That picture was copied from a magazine cover.   _____

14. Tennis occupyied much of their vacation time.   _____

15. The problem can be solved by multipling the last two
    numbers.   _____

2

Up in Smoke

The sight of typewritten words probably doesn't stop you in your tracks. But the sight of a typewritten message across the sky very well might. That's why Greg Stinis and his skytypers have gone to the air. They want their words to be hard to miss.

Skytyping is not as common as skywriting but it's being used more and more. Skywriters make written words. Skytypers make printed words to display their messages. The art of skytyping was invented in 1949. The skytypers use World War II planes because they have large engines that make great amounts of heat. The heat is needed to melt a substance called paraffin. This process results in a white smoke that is used to write messages.

The skytypers employ a series of dashes to form letters. They fly five planes in close formation. A computer-controlled device automatically lets out puffs of smoke from each of the planes at the same time. These puffs form letters. Each letter is as large as the Empire State Building—1,200 feet tall. These heavenly billboards often stretch over five miles of sky! Skytyped words can relay a message to those miles away. On a clear day millions of people can see one skytyped message.

Greg and the other four skytypers often write ads for suntan lotion, cars, cameras, films, and records. And for those who easily tire of greeting cards, the skytypers have written countless "Happy Birthdays," "I Love You's," and "Congratulations." Once, they even played a flying tic-tac-toe game. Skytyping will probably be around for a long time. The message is hard to miss!

REVIEWING YOUR READING

Circle the letter beside the word or phrase that best completes the sentence.

1. Skytyping was invented in

   a. 1449.
   b. 1494.
   c. 1949.
   d. 1994.

2. The skytypers use World War II planes because they

   a. fly at a faster speed than other planes.
   b. fly at a higher altitude than other planes.
   c. make great amounts of electricity.
   d. make great amounts of heat.

3. The skytypers fly

   a. five planes in close formation.
   b. ten planes in close formation.
   c. fifteen planes in close formation.
   d. twenty planes in close formation.

4. The puffs of smoke are released by

   a. a person in the rear of the plane.
   b. a computer-controlled instrument.
   c. the wings.
   d. the wheels.

5. Skytyped letters are as large as

   a. the Statue of Liberty.
   b. the Empire State Building.
   c. an airplane.
   d. a billboard.

6. To form letters, skytypers employ a series of

   a. curved lines.
   b. loops and swirls.
   c. dashes.
   d. dots and curves.

7. According to the story, you can conclude that

   a. skytyping is different from skywriting.
   b. skytyping is out of style.
   c. skywriting is the newest type of advertisement.
   d. skywriting is done from the ground.

8. Another title for this story could be

   a. Greg Stinis—Skytyper.
   b. Skytyping.
   c. Skywriting.
   d. The Flying Tic-tac-toe Game.

FIGURING THE FACTS

Decide whether the following statements are true or false. Write *T* on the line if the statement is true. If the statement is false, cross out the incorrect word or phrase in the sentence. Then write the correct word or phrase on the line to make the statement true.

1. Skytyping is being used less and less these days.   _____

2. The skytyping planes release black smoke.   _____

3. The smoke is produced from paraffin.   _____

4. Skytyping is more common than skywriting.   _____

5. The puffs of smoke form letters.   _____

6. A skytyped message is printed close to the ground.   _____

7. The skytypers fly seven planes in formation.   _____

8. On a clear day millions of people can see one skytyped message.   _____

9. Skytypers never print ads.   _____

10. The story tells us that there was once a flying chess game.   _____

WHAT'S YOUR OPINION?

1. Why do you think skytyping is becoming so popular?

_____

_____

_____

_____

_____

2. Do you think reading a skytyped message is more exciting than reading a message written on paper? Why or why not?

_____

_____

_____

_____

_____

DEVELOPING SPELLING SKILLS

Study List

alloys
annoyance
betrayed
conveying
decayed
decoys
destroyed
disobeyed
displaying
employer
journeys
relaying
strayed
surveying
swaying

The following words appear in the reading selection.

display   employ   relay

All of these words contain a final *y* that is preceded by a vowel. Notice in the Study List words that when we add a suffix, the *y* remains the same.

Rule: **When a word ends in a final *y* that is preceded by a vowel, the word is not changed when adding a suffix. (This rule also applies when forming the plural of the word.)**

Examples: displaying   employers   relayed

On your left is a Study List of words. Each has been formed by adding a suffix to a word that ends in a final *y* preceded by a vowel.

SKILL DRILL 1

Add the suffix to the word ending in *y* to form words from the Study List. Write your answers on the lines provided.

1. display + ing = _____

2. journey + s = _____

3. survey + ing = _____

4. sway + ing = _____

5. annoy + ance = _____

6. convey + ing = _____

7. decoy + s = _____

8. employ + er = _____

9. relay + ing = _____

10. stray + ed = _____

11. alloy + s = _____

12. betray + ed = _____

13. decay + ed = _____

14. destroy + ed = _____

15. disobey + ed = _____

SKILL DRILL 2

The following are short definitions of words from the Study List. Fill the blanks with words from the Study List that match the definitions. If you need help, check the Mini-Dictionary in the back of this book.

1. Metals made by mixing two or more metals _____

2. Transporting or carrying something—a word that means the same as relaying _____

3. Was unfaithful to something or gave away a secret _____

4. Swinging back and forth _____

5. Wandered or roamed away _____

6. Refused or failed to obey _____

7. Taking something and carrying it farther—a word that means the same as conveying _____

8. Long trips or travels _____

9. A person or firm that hires someone to work _____

10. Rotted; losing strength or beauty _____

11. Things used to lure or tempt someone into danger _____

12. Something that bothers or disturbs you _____

13. Showing or exposing to view _____

14. Broken into pieces; ended _____

15. Looking over or viewing something; skimming _____

SKILL DRILL 3

Complete each sentence by adding a suffix to the word in parentheses to form a Study List word.

1. The workers will be (survey) _____ the land tomorrow.

2. Tom (disobey) _____ the traffic rule by jay walking.

3. The puppies (stray) _____ onto the beach.

4. The cypress trees are (sway) _____ in the breeze.

5. The trucks will be (convey) _____ these supplies.

6. Elaine (betray) _____ the trust of her friends.

7. These metals are (alloy) _____ .

8. Mrs. Smith (destroy) _____ the copy of the letter.

9. The department store will be (display) _____ the product tomorrow.

10. Those airplanes are an (annoy) _____ to the students.

11. The hunters hid their (decoy) _____ under the bushes.

12. Ralph's back teeth have become (decay) _____ from not brushing.

13. This company is an equal opportunity (employ) _____ .

14. The club has taken many (journey) _____ to the seaside.

15. These wires are always (relay) _____ messages across the country.

SKILL DRILL 4

Answer the following questions by using words from the Study List.

Which words end with the suffix *ing*?

1. _____   2. _____

3. _____   4. _____

5. _____

Which word ends with the suffix *er*?

6. _____

Which words appear in their plural form?

7. _____   8. _____

9. _____

Which words end with the suffix *ed*?

10. _____   11. _____

12. _____   13. _____

14. _____

Which words end with the suffix *ance*?

15. _____

WORD GAME 2

All of the letters from the words in the Study List appear in this puzzle. Cross out the letters of the puzzle as you use them to spell the Study List words. There will be enough letters left over to answer the question below.

```
            A  A  A
         A  A  A  A  A
      A  B  B  C  C  C  C
   D  D  D  D  D  D  D  D  D
   D  E  E  E  E  E  E  E  E  E
E  E  E  E  E  E  G  G  G  G  I
I  I  I  I  I  I  J  L  L  L  L  M
N  N  N  N  N  N  N  N  N  O  O  O
O  O  O  O  O  P  P  P  R  R  R  R
   R  R  S  S  S  S  S  S  S  S
      T  T  T  U  U  U  V  V  W
         Y  Y  Y  Y  Y  Y  Y
            Y  Y  Y  Y  Y
               Y  Y  Y
```

Study List

alloys
annoyance
betrayed
conveying
decayed
decoys
destroyed
disobeyed
displaying
employer
journeys
relaying
strayed
surveying
swaying

Where would you begin to look to find the skytypers? _____

HOW WELL CAN YOU SPELL?

Try to take this practice test without looking back at Lesson 2. After you have finished, check your work against the Study List. Correct any mistakes you have made.

A. One word in each of the following pairs of words is spelled incorrectly. Circle that word and spell it correctly on the line provided.

1. conveing, swaying   _____

2. displaying, disobeyied   _____

3. decaied, relayed   _____

4. destroyed, annoiance   _____

5. betrayed, journies   _____

6. decoyies, strayed   _____

7. alloyies, employer   _____

8. surveing, relaying   _____

B. In each of the following sentences, one word is spelled incorrectly. Find the word. Then spell it correctly on the line provided.

9. The storm destroyied all of the homes on the coast.   _____

10. The students are proudly displaing their school colors.   _____

11. The wind was so strong, even the telephone poles were swaing.   _____

12. The robber's guilt was betrayied by the mud on his shoes.   _____

13. Three young scouts strayied away from camp today.   _____

14. This employier is very generous to the workers.   _____

15. The girls will be relaing the message at the meeting.   _____

Cliff Hanger

"The way to eat an elephant is one bite at a time." Those were the words Beverly Johnson repeated to herself. Inch by inch she made her way up the steep mountain wall in California's Yosemite National Park. Beverly Johnson was climbing a cliff called El Capitan. It is one of the most overpowering walls in the world. From bottom to top the distance is 3,604 feet. That's as long as ten football fields—straight up! Beverly Johnson climbed the mighty cliff alone. She is the first woman ever to do so.

The climb usually requires a team of two or three people. And it takes about a week to reach the top. Six months before Beverly's adventure, three climbers tried to conquer El Capitan. They fell to their deaths.

The "solo" trip for Beverly was doubly difficult. She first had to climb about 100 feet. That was her first "pitch." Climbers measure how far they are climbing by what they call "pitches." A "pitch" is usually the length of their safety ropes. Beverly then drove a metal stake called a piton into the rock. After attaching her ropes to the piton, she lowered herself back down to get her gear. She then went back up, fastened her gear, and started to work on her next "pitch." She had to go up and down each pitch twice, pulling out the metal stakes as she went. Beverly made 27 pitches in all.

Her pouch of supplies included cheeses, fruits, water, and a "bat tent." That's a type of hammock that is anchored to the wall. Beverly made no comment about how well she slept hanging off the cliff. But during her climb, a small earthquake took place. When asked if she felt the quake, Beverly replied, "No, I thought it might have been my knees shaking."

REVIEWING YOUR READING

Circle the letter beside the word or phrase that best completes the sentence.

1. Beverly Johnson climbed a

   a. tall building.
   b. mountain wall.
   c. football stadium.
   d. large tree.

2. Beverly made her climb

   a. alone.
   b. with one other person.
   c. with two other people.
   d. with three other people.

3. Three climbers fell off the cliff

   a. six years before Beverly's climb.
   b. six months before Beverly's climb.
   c. after Beverly's climb.

   d. during Beverly's climb.

4. Climbers measure how far they are climbing by what they call

   a. pitons.
   b. gear.
   c. lengths.
   d. pitches.

5. Beverly's climb was doubly difficult because she had to

   a. take twice the gear.
   b. go up and down each "pitch" twice.
   c. bring twice as much food with her.
   d. drive in twice as many pitons.

6. A piton is a

   a. rope.
   b. pitch.
   c. metal stake.
   d. hammer.

7. During Beverly's climb there was

   a. an earthquake.
   b. a tornado.
   c. a thunderstorm.
   d. a snowstorm.

8. According to the story, you can conclude that Beverly

   a. enjoys risk and adventure.
   b. is afraid of heights.
   c. is not athletic.
   d. prefers to climb with a large group of people.

FIGURING THE FACTS

Decide whether the following statements are true or false. Write *T* on the line if the statement is true. If the statement is false, cross out the incorrect word or phrase in the sentence. Then write the correct word or phrase on the line to make the statement true.

1. The cliff Beverly climbed was called "Elephant."   _____

2. The cliff is as long as ten football fields.   _____

3. Beverly made her climb in Yosemite National Park.   _____

4. It usually takes about three weeks to reach the top.   _____

5. A pitch is usually the length of a climber's tent.   _____

6. Beverly made her climb in one pitch.   _____

7. Beverly's supplies included cheeses, fruits, and water.   _____

8. At night, Beverly slept in a cat tent.   _____

9. Beverly said she slept while hanging off the cliff.   _____

10. During her climb, Beverly felt an earthquake.   _____

WHAT'S YOUR OPINION?

1. What do you think Beverly meant when she said, "The way to eat an elephant is one bite at a time"?

   _____

   _____

   _____

   _____

   _____

2. If you could be the first person to climb a mountain alone, would you do it? Why or why not?

   _____

   _____

   _____

   _____

   _____

DEVELOPING SPELLING SKILLS

Study List

Singular	Plural
adventure	adventures
ambulance	ambulances
budget	budgets
characteristic	characteristics
cheese	cheeses
crutch	crutches
hatchet	hatchets
inch	inches
opinion	opinions
pouch	pouches
radish	radishes
sandwich	sandwiches
sheriff	sheriffs
sketch	sketches
stitch	stitches

In this lesson we will look at how to change some words to the plural form. For example, we know that to change a word that ends in *y* like *apology* to the plural, we change the final *y* to *i* and add *es*. The plural of *apology* is *apologies*. In the next few chapters we will be learning the different ways that words become plural.

Rule: **Most words form their plural by adding *s* to the singular form.**

Examples:	*Singular*	*Plural*
	adventure	adventures
	budget	budgets
	cheese	cheeses

But words that end in *ch* or *sh* form their plurals by adding *es*.

Examples:	*Singular*	*Plural*
	inch	inches
	pouch	pouches
	radish	radishes

Rule: **If a word ends in *ch* or *sh*, the plural is formed by adding *es*.**

Above is a Study List of words. Both the singular and plural forms are listed. It is important to know both.

SKILL DRILL 1

Change each of the following singular nouns to the plural. Write your answers on the lines provided.

1. hatchet _____

2. sandwich _____

3. sketch _____

4. inch _____

5. pouch _____

6. ambulance _____

7. characteristic_____

8. radish _____

9. sheriff _____

10. stitch _____

11. opinion _____

12. adventure _____

13. budget _____

14. cheese _____

15. crutch _____

SKILL DRILL 2

The following are short definitions of words from the Study List. The definitions are of the words in their singular form. Write the *singular form* of the Study List word that matches the definition. If you need help, check the Mini-Dictionary in the back of this book.

1. A solid food made from milk _____

2. A plan for spending time or money _____

3. A vehicle used to carry sick people _____

4. An unusual or exciting experience _____

5. A law enforcement officer _____

6. A support to help a lame person walk _____

7. A rough or quickly done drawing _____

8. A loop of thread made while sewing _____

9. Two slices of bread with filling between such as meat or cheese _____

10. A small, crisp, red vegetable _____

11. A bag or sack _____

12. What a person thinks _____

13. A measure of length _____

14. A quality that shows how a person or thing is different from others _____

15. A small axe that is used with one hand _____

SKILL DRILL 3

Fill in each blank with the plural of the noun in parentheses to form a Study List word.

1. Help yourself to the (cheese) _____.

2. The (stitch) _____ in my jacket are coming apart.

3. Please get Janice her (crutch) _____.

4. Milk and some (sandwich) _____ are in the refrigerator.

5. Dad pulled the two (hatchet) _____ out of the tree.

6. What this salad needs is some (radish) _____.

7. Kangaroos are one of the few animals with (pouch) _____.

8. The students gave their (opinion) _____ at the meeting.

9. Next year the clerks will have to balance their (budget) _____.

10. There was a line of (ambulance) _____ outside the hospital.

11. Each day is full of (adventure) _____, if you look for them.

12. Seven (sheriff) _____ will be at the meeting.

13. The artist showed us several (sketch) _____.

14. She is three (inch) _____ taller than I.

15. Courtesy and friendliness are the (characteristic) _____ of a good salesperson.

SKILL DRILL 4

Answer the following questions by using words from the Study List.

Which words end with the letters *ts*?

1. _____   2. _____

Which word ends with the letters *shes*?

3. _____

Which words end with the letters *ches*?

4. _____   5. _____

6. _____   7. _____

8. _____   9. _____

Which word ends with the letters *ces*?

11. _____

Which word ends with the letters *ns*?

12. _____

Which word ends with the letters *res*?

13. _____

Which word ends with the letters *fs*?

14. _____

Which word ends with the letters *cs*?

15. _____

Study List

adventures
ambulances
budgets
characteristics
cheeses
crutches
hatchets
inches
opinions
pouches
radishes
sandwiches
sheriffs
sketches
stitches

WORD GAME 3

The plural form of the words from the Study List are scrambled on the left. Unscramble each word and write it correctly in the spaces on the right. If you unscramble the words correctly, you will find the answer to the puzzle question by reading the shaded column downward. Write your answer on the line below.

S N O P O N I I
S D T V A E N U E R
S E C S E H E

S O H C E P U
S T I H C S E T
S E H C T E K S
S I N E H C
S C A R A H C C I T R E T I S

S R D A I S H E
S T A H C H E T

S C H I D A N W S E

S T H C U R C E
S F I R H E F S
S N A L U B M A E C
S U B G D T E

How did Beverly Johnson make it up El Capitan? _____

HOW WELL CAN YOU SPELL?

Try to take this practice test without looking back at Lesson 3. After you have finished, check your work against the Study List. Correct any mistakes you have made.

A. One word in each of the following pairs of words is spelled incorrectly. Circle that word and spell it correctly on the line provided.

1. ambulanses, sandwiches   _____

2. inches, sheriffes   _____

3. characteristices, radishes   _____

4. pouchs, hatchets   _____

5. opinions, crutchs   _____

6. stitchs, cheeses   _____

7. adventurs, ambulances   _____

8. budgetes, sketches   _____

B. In each of the following sentences, one word is spelled incorrectly. Find that word. Then spell it correctly on the line provided.

9. Thelma has several opiniones on that subject.   _____

10. We will be having peanut butter sandwichs for lunch.   _____

11. Shirley needs a few more inchs of ribbon for the package.   _____

12. Be sure to buy some radishs at the market.   _____

13. Ken will be serving fruits and cheesees tonight.   _____

14. The art class will be doing sketchs this week.   _____

15. The workers found several old hatchetes in the basement.   _____

The Moose Is Loose!

You'll find them roaming hills and valleys from Alaska and British Columbia to Nova Scotia and Maine. Their deep bellow can be heard for miles around. Some people describe the noise as a deep a-e-i-o-u. It may sound terrible to you and me, but to another moose it means "hello."

The moose is the largest member of the deer family. Moose can weigh up to a ton. With all that weight, you'd think they would have difficulty moving at all. But they can run at speeds of 35 miles per hour! During the warm weather months, moose like to be near water. They are excellent swimmers, able to travel for a dozen miles without stopping. They are even good at high diving. Some moose can dive from heights of 20 feet.

Each spring, the male, or bull moose, grows a crown of majestic antlers. Unlike the horns of other animals, which are hardened skin, moose antlers are made entirely of bone. Aside from their beauty, they also serve a purpose. Antlers attract females. In addition, they are used as weapons. If one bull tries to steal another bull's mate, trouble begins. Sometimes moose lock horns in battle. But more often than not, they shake the bushes with their antlers and make a lot of noise. This is supposed to frighten the intruder. It seems that even the moose like to avoid fighting. When first grown, moose antlers are covered with a velvet-like skin. Eventually, the moose will rub them against trees to remove the "velvet." Then the white bone will become stained brown. When winter comes and the antlers are no longer needed, the moose sheds them. As spring approaches, the cycle starts anew.

Although moose are now plentiful, they were once in danger of extinction. Thanks to conservation, these grand creatures still roam North America.

REVIEWING YOUR READING

Circle the letter beside the word or phrase that best completes the sentence.

1. Moose can be found living in

   a. South America.
   b. North America.
   c. Mexico.
   d. the southern United States.

2. The noise a moose makes can be described as

   a. a high sharp sound.
   b. a loud coughing noise.
   c. a hooting sound.
   d. a deep bellow.

3. During the summer, moose like to be near

   a. mountains.
   b. valleys.
   c. water.
   d. caves.

4. Some moose can

   a. swim for 50 miles.
   b. dive 20 feet.
   c. swim 100 miles.
   d. dive 135 feet.

5. Moose antlers are made entirely of

   a. bone.
   b. skin.
   c. wood.
   d. velvet.

6. Each year the moose

   a. grows a new set of antlers.
   b. sheds his fur.
   c. sheds his skin.
   d. grows longer antlers.

7. You can come to the conclusion that male moose

   a. enjoy fighting.
   b. probably don't like to fight.
   c. are afraid of water.
   d. are afraid of noise.

8. You can come to the conclusion that

   a. there are only a few moose still living.
   b. there are many moose in the wild.
   c. moose are now extinct.
   d. moose were once extinct.

FIGURING THE FACTS

Decide whether the following statements are true or false. Write *T* on the line if the statement is true. If the statement is false, cross out the incorrect word or phrase in the sentence. Then write the correct word or phrase on the line to make the statement true.

1. The male moose is called a bull. _____

2. The moose often makes a sound like an owl. _____

3. A moose can swim for many miles. _____

4. The moose may be found in Nova Scotia. _____

5. The moose's antlers are used to pick food. _____

6. Sometimes the antlers are used as weapons. _____

7. Moose antlers are exactly like other animals' horns. _____

8. Antlers are sometimes covered wtih velvet-like skin. _____

9. Female moose sometimes lock horns in battle. _____

10. A moose can run 35 miles per hour. _____

WHAT'S YOUR OPINION?

1. At one time the moose was almost extinct. Why is it important to help and protect animals?

_____

_____

_____

_____

_____

2. The moose only fights when he has to. Do you think this is a good way to be? Why?

_____

_____

_____

_____

_____

_____

DEVELOPING SPELLING SKILLS

Study List

Singular	Plural
activity	activities
ambulance	ambulances
bush	bushes
class	classes
fox	foxes
hatchet	hatchets
magazine	magazines
match	matches
parade	parades
reflex	reflexes
schedule	schedules
speech	speeches
trophy	trophies
valley	valleys
wish	wishes

In this lesson we will review the rules we've learned about plural forms. We will learn a new rule that explains how words ending in *x* form the plural.

Rule: **Words that end in *x* form their plural by adding *es*.**

Example: *Singular*   *Plural*
reflex   reflexes

Here is a review of the other rules we've learned.

Rule: **Most words form their plural by adding *s* to the singular form.**

Example: *Singular*   *Plural*
parade   parades

Rule: **Words that end in *ch* or *sh* form their plural by adding *es*.**

Example: *Singular*   *Plural*
match   matches

Rule: **Words that end in *y* preceded by a consonant change the *y* to *i* and add *es*.**

Example: *Singular*   *Plural*
activity   activities

Above is a Study List of words. Both singular and plural forms are listed. As you look at each word in the Study List, try to remember which of the rules mentioned above applies to the plural form.

SKILL DRILL 1

Change each of the following singular nouns to the plural. Write your answers on the lines provided.

1. parade _____
2. schedule _____
3. trophy _____
4. activity _____
5. bush _____
6. fox _____
7. magazine _____

8. reflex _____
9. speech _____
10. valley _____
11. ambulance _____
12. class _____
13. hatchet _____
14. match _____

15. wish _____

SKILL DRILL 2

The following are short definitions of words from the Study List. The definitions are of the words in their singular form. Write the *singular form* of the Study List word that matches the definition. If you need help, check the Mini-Dictionary.

1. A public talk _____
2. A written or printed statement of details _____
3. An automatic response _____
4. A march or display _____
5. A wild animal that is sly and crafty _____
6. A meeting of a group of students and a teacher _____
7. A woody plant that is smaller than a tree _____
8. Vehicle used to carry sick people _____
9. Vigorous or strenuous action or movement _____
10. A person or thing that goes well with another person or thing _____
11. A regular publication containing stories and articles _____
12. A small axe that is used with one hand _____
13. An expression of a desire or want _____
14. Low land between hills or mountains _____
15. A prize for the winner of a contest _____

SKILL DRILL 3

Fill in each blank with the plural of the noun in parentheses to form a Study List word.

1. There will be two (trophy) _____ for each winner.

2. Debbie would like to stay and listen to the (speech) _____.

3. When you're at the train station, please pick up some (schedule) _____.

4. Would you like some (magazine) _____ to read on the plane?

5. We will need a few (hatchet) _____ for cutting these trees.

6. Twirlers must have good (reflex) _____.

7. There will be three (parade) _____ on Tuesday.

8. We have a family of (fox) _____ living behind the house.

9. The camp has many (activity) _____ for the students.

10. In the play, the colors of the girls' dresses were good (match) _____.

11. The art (class) _____ will be meeting next week.

12. Ed got a job trimming the (bush) _____ in the park.

13. Our hospital has several (ambulance) _____ ready for emergencies.

14. I hope that all of Joan's (wish) _____ come true.

15. On the other side of those hills, there are several large (valley) _____.

SKILL DRILL 4

Answer the following questions by using words from the Study List.

Which words end in *xes*?

1. _____   2. _____

Which words end in *ches*?

3. _____   4. _____

Which words end in *shes*?

5. _____   6. _____

Which word ends in *ses*?   Which word ends in *ces*?

7. _____   8. _____

Which word ends in *eys*?

9. _____

Which word ends in *les*?

10. _____

Which word ends in *nes*?

11. _____

Which word ends in *des*?

12. _____

Which words end in *ies*?

13. _____

14. _____

Which word ends in *ets*?

15. _____

Study List	
Singular	*Plural*
activity	activities
ambulance	ambulances
bush	bushes
class	classes
fox	foxes
hatchet	hatchets
magazine	magazines
match	matches
parade	parades
reflex	reflexes
schedule	schedules
speech	speeches
trophy	trophies
valley	valleys
wish	wishes

WORD GAME 4

The words from the Study List are used in this puzzle. The numbers of the clues match the numbers in the puzzle.

ACROSS
3. Actions or movements
5. Hopes and dreams
9. Reading materials
11. Learning places
14. Automatic responses
15. Prizes

DOWN
1. Vehicles for medical emergencies
2. Firestarters
4. Public talks
6. Timetables
7. Axes
8. Marches
10. Small shrubs
12. Low lands between hills
13. Crafty animals

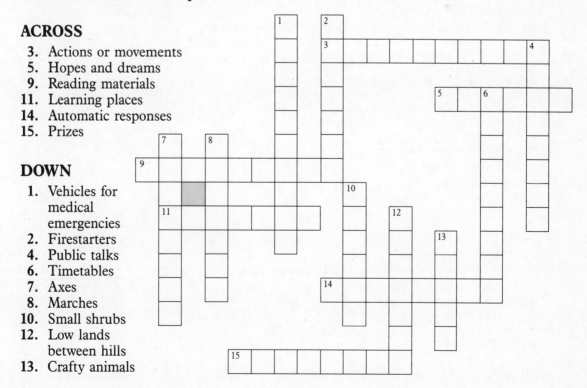

HOW WELL CAN YOU SPELL?

Try to take this practice test without looking back at Lesson 4. After you have finished, check your work against the Study List. Correct any mistakes you have made.

A. One word in each of the following pairs of words is spelled incorrectly. Circle that word and spell it correctly on the line provided.

1. wishs, magazines   _____

2. hatchetes, parades   _____

3. activity, foxs   _____

4. reflexs, trophies   _____

5. matches, ambulancies   _____

6. vallies, bushes   _____

7. classes, scheduls   _____

8. speechs, parade   _____

B. In each of the following sentences, one word is spelled incorrectly. Find that word. Then spell it correctly on the line provided.

9. There will be several activitys scheduled for today.   _____

10. Elaine has twelve trophys in her collection.   _____

11. Baton twirlers are often seen performing in parads.   _____

12. Jack left the magazins on the shelf in the library.   _____

13. The frightened animal was hiding in the bushs.   _____

14. Billy's shirt always matchs his pants.   _____

15. My cooking classis will begin early next week.   _____

Cowkids

A proud horse prances into the arena. Its rider struggles to hold a huge American flag that snaps in the breeze. Echoes of "Yahoo" and "Yippee" explode from the crowd. Parading close behind is a seemingly endless line of riders on horseback. Friendly young faces shine from beneath ten-gallon hats. At any other rodeo, there are pens of horses and buffaloes, and cowpokes sitting on wood fences. This special event is the National High School Rodeo.

Each year since 1949, teenagers from all over the United States and Canada have come together for the world's largest rodeo. With headquarters in Denver, Colorado, this rodeo is held in a different location each year. They meet to pick the best all- round cowkids and to have an all-round good time.

Some of the events include calf roping and steer wrestling. One of the wildest competitions is reserved for cowgirls only. It's called goat tying. To begin, a goat is placed in the middle of the arena. The contestant races to the goat on horseback. She must jump off the horse, catch the goat, and throw it down. Then she must tie three of the goat's legs together. Of course, the goat is not very happy about being tied up. The result is usually a tornado of dust and flying hooves.

A time of ten seconds in the goat tying event is very quick. But a teenager named Betty Joles from Arizona has done it in a little more than seven seconds! For a time like that, Betty has to get lots of practice. She also must be in top physical condition. The event requires speed and dexterity.

Why does she do it? She's a competitor. And that's what the National High School Rodeo is all about—competition. There are over a thousand competitors in all, and the number is growing every year. Ride 'em, cowkids!

REVIEWING YOUR READING

Circle the letter beside the word or phrase that best completes the sentence.

1. The National High School Rodeo begins with a

   a. movie.
   b. parade.
   c. fireworks display.
   d. race.

2. The teenagers who take part in the rodeo are all from

   a. Canada.
   b. Kansas.
   c. the United States.
   d. the United States and Canada.

3. The goat-tying competition is reserved for

   a. cowgirls only.
   b. cowboys only.
   c. goats only.
   d. adults only.

4. In the goat-tying competition, contestants race to the goat on

   a. goats.
   b. mules.
   c. donkeys.
   d. horses.

5. Betty Joles won the

   a. steer-wrestling event.
   b. goat-tying competition.
   c. horse-jumping event.
   d. goat-wrestling competition.

6. The goat-tying event requires speed and dexterity. The word *dexterity* in this sentence most probably means

   a. riding ability.
   b. know-how and skill.
   c. roping skill.
   d. quick thinking.

7. You can conclude that rodeo competitors are

   a. in top physical condition.
   b. usually poor students.
   c. not good with animals.
   d. also very good students.

8. According to the story, you can conclude that teenagers take part in the rodeo because they like to

   a. feed the animals.
   b. march in parades.
   c. compete.
   d. tie up the animals.

FIGURING THE FACTS

Decide whether the following statements are true or false. Write *T* on the line if the statement is true. If the statement is false, change the statement to make it true. Cross out the incorrect word or phrase in the sentence. Then, if necessary, write the correct word or phrase on the line.

1. At a rodeo, you might see cowpokes sitting on wood fences.   _____

2. The National High School Rodeo is the world's smallest rodeo.   _____

3. The National High School Rodeo has been happening since 1949.   _____

4. One of the fastest events is the calf relay race.   _____

5. There are over three million competitors at the rodeo.   _____

6. In goat tying, all four of the goat's legs must be tied.   _____

7. There are over a thousand competitors in the National High School Rodeo.   _____

8. The goats do not like to be tied up.   _____

9. The number of contestants in the rodeo is growing every year.   _____

10. During the National High School Rodeo, the contestants stage a parade.   _____

WHAT'S YOUR OPINION?

1. Why do you think more and more teenagers are getting involved in the rodeo?

_____

_____

_____

2. During the rodeo, the animals are not hurt. Do you think it is all right to tie up the animals? Why or why not?

_____

_____

_____

DEVELOPING SPELLING SKILLS

Study List

Singular	Plural
banjo	banjos
buffalo	buffaloes
hero	heroes
piano	pianos
portfolio	portfolios
potato	potatoes
radio	radios
rodeo	rodeos
shampoo	shampoos
soprano	sopranos
stereo	stereos
studio	studios
tomato	tomatoes
tornado	tornadoes
volcano	volcanoes

When changing words to the plural, we must be especially careful of words that end with the letter *o*. Here are some words taken from the reading selection. Some form plurals differently from others.

Examples:

Singular	Plural
rodeo	rodeos
buffalo	buffaloes
tornado	tornadoes

Notice that the word *rodeo* forms its plural by simply adding *s*. The words *tornado* and *buffalo* form their plurals by adding *es*. This is because tornado and buffalo end in *o* preceded by a consonant. **Remember: a, e, i, o, u, and sometimes y are vowels. All the other letters of the alphabet are consonants.**

Rule: **If a noun ends in *o* preceded by a vowel, add *s* to form the plural. If a noun ends in *o* preceded by a consonant, add *es* to form the plural.**

Exception: **Musical terms and instruments that end in *o* form their plurals by adding *s*.**

For example: banjos, pianos, or sopranos.

Above is a Study List of words. Both the singular and plural forms are listed. It is most important to know both.

SKILL DRILL 1

Circle the last two letters in each of the following words. Then write the plural form of each word on the line provided.

1. rodeo _____   8. radio _____

2. potato _____   9. portfolio _____

3. piano _____   10. studio _____

4. stereo _____   11. hero _____

5. buffalo _____   12. banjo _____

6. volcano _____   13. tornado _____

7. tomato _____   14. soprano _____

15. shampoo _____

SKILL DRILL 2

The following are short definitions of words from the Study List. The definitions are for the words in their singular form. Write the *singular form* of the Study List word that matches the definition. If you need help, check the Mini-Dictionary.

1. A soap used to wash hair _____

2. A contest in riding horses or roping cattle _____

3. A large, shaggy animal with strong legs; a bison _____

4. A way of sending or receiving sounds by electric waves _____

5. A white vegetable _____

6. A portable case for papers, or a briefcase _____

7. A juicy, red vegetable _____

8. A violent and destructive storm; a whirlwind _____

9. A large musical instrument played by striking the keys on its keyboard _____

10. A workroom for a painter or other artist _____

11. A person admired for bravery or great deeds _____

12. A record player or radio that brings sound from two directions _____

13. A singer with the highest singing voice there is _____

14. A hand-held, stringed musical instrument _____

15. A mountain that expels steam and lava _____

SKILL DRILL 3

Fill in each blank with the plural of the noun in parentheses to form a Study List word.

1. This afternoon we will go shopping for (radio) _____.

2. Many (tornado) _____ have been spotted in the Kansas area.

3. This year's crop of (tomato) _____ will be excellent.

4. Art students may leave their (portfolio) _____ in the hall.

5. The dinner will include fish and (potato) _____.

6. There are still many (buffalo) _____ roaming the West.

7. Ginny has been attending (rodeo) _____ since she was three.

8. There are several (stereo) _____ to choose from.

9. All of the astronauts are (hero) _____.

10. There are several (volcano) _____ on the island.

11. Auditions for (soprano) _____ will be held today.

12. We have two (studio) _____ available in this building.

13. The orchestra will be using two (piano) _____.

14. You will find several (shampoo) _____ on the shelf.

15. For the duet, we will need two (banjo) _____.

SKILL DRILL 4

Answer the following questions by using words from the Study List. You must write both the singular and plural forms.

| Singular | Plural |

Which three words are either musical instruments or musical terms?

1. _____   _____

2. _____   _____

3. _____   _____

Which words are not musical terms but end in an *o* preceded by a consonant?

4. _____   _____

5. _____   _____

	Singular	**Plural**
6.	_____	_____
7.	_____	_____
8.	_____	_____
9.	_____	_____

Which words end in *o* preceded by a vowel?

10.	_____	_____
11.	_____	_____
12.	_____	_____
13.	_____	_____
14.	_____	_____
15.	_____	_____

Study List

banjos
buffaloes
heroes
pianos
portfolios
potatoes
radios
rodeos
shampoos
sopranos
stereos
studios
tomatoes
tornadoes
volcanoes

WORD GAME 5

This is a crossword puzzle without clues! Study the length and spelling of each word in the Study List. Then figure out which words fit in the spaces.

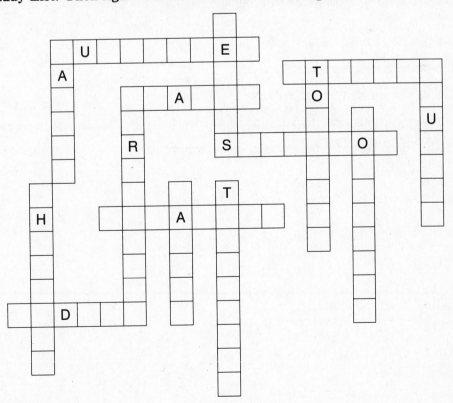

HOW WELL CAN YOU SPELL?

Try to take this practice test without looking back at Lesson 5. After you have finished, check your work against the Study List. Correct any mistakes you have made.

A. One word in each of the following pairs of words is spelled incorrectly. Circle that word and spell it correctly on the line provided.

1. tornado, pianoes   _____

2. shampooes, studios   _____

3. stereoes, banjos   _____

4. rodeo, portfolioes   _____

5. radioes, heroes   _____

6. banjo, sopranoes   _____

7. volcanos, tomato   _____

8. potatoes, buffalos   _____

B. In each of the following sentences, one word is spelled incorrectly. Find that word. Then spell it correctly on the line provided.

9. The new building will have two dance studioes.   _____

10. I'll be earning extra money picking potatos during vacation.   _____

11. Laura has two banjoes in her collection.   _____

12. Ted and Janet are the heros of the team.   _____

13. There have been many teenage rodeoes in Texas.   _____

14. Don't forget to put some tomatos in the salad.   _____

15. Over the years, tornados have caused great damage to lives and property.   _____

Greenpeace

"We've had our people in some very flaky situations. It's a small miracle that no one has gotten killed," says Bob Hunter, speaking for the group called Greenpeace. The group is a body of people who are determined to stop the senseless killing of animals. Sometimes they even risk their own lives to protect wildlife.

Their main work has been in saving whales. Some countries still hunt whales, using large, modern whaling ships. The Greenpeace ships patrol the oceans. When the Greenpeacers find a whale about to be killed by hunters, they go into action. They launch small motor-driven rafts and get between the whales and the hunters. Whale hunters can't fire their harpoons without risking injury to a Greenpeace member. A harpoon is a long spear with a knife-sharp edge. Once, while protecting a mother whale and her calf, the Greenpeacers were fired upon. A harpoon came close to hitting the courageous volunteers.

Lately, things have changed. Whalers want to avoid trouble. They hold their fire when they see a Greenpeace raft. Greenpeace members have even boarded a Russian whaling ship. Instead of arguing, they handed out "Save the Whales" T-shirts to the crew. It seems that Greenpeace is not only saving whales but also making friends.

The group was begun in the late 1960s. A few Canadians and Americans joined together and called themselves the Greenpeace Foundation. Their numbers have grown steadily ever since. Today, they are a multinational organization known as Greenpeace International. Their home base is Lewes, England. They have over 250,000 members from all over the world.

REVIEWING YOUR READING

Circle the letter beside the word or phrase that best completes the sentence.

1. Greenpeace is a body of people who are determined to save

   a. whaling ships.
   b. whalers.
   c. wildlife.
   d. national parks.

2. The Greenpeace ships

   a. hunt whales.
   b. patrol the oceans.
   c. kill hunters.
   d. were sunk.

3. In trying to save the whales, the Greenpeacers have

   a. captured whales.
   b. captured hunters.
   c. gotten between the whales and their calves.
   d. gotten between the whales and the hunters.

4. A harpoon is a

   a. big whale.
   b. small boat.
   c. long spear.
   d. huge raft.

5. The whalers want to

   a. avoid trouble.
   b. hurt the Greenpeacers.
   c. destroy the Greenpeace ships.
   d. form an organization of their own.

6. Greenpeacers once boarded a Russian ship and handed out

   a. food.
   b. T-shirts.
   c. harpoons.
   d. rafts.

7. The home base for Greenpeace is

   a. Chicago, Illinois.
   b. Mexico City, Mexico.
   c. Lewes, England.
   d. Vancouver, British Columbia.

8. According to the story, you can conclude that Greenpeacers are

   a. not protecting whales.
   b. protecting hunters.
   c. saving whales and making friends.
   d. selling whales to hunters.

FIGURING THE FACTS

Decide whether the following statements are true or false. Write *T* on the line if the statement is true. If the statement is false, cross out the incorrect word or phrase in the sentence. Then write the correct word or phrase on the line to make the statement true.

1. Sometimes Greenpeacers risk their own lives to save animals.   _____

2. The main work of Greenpeace is saving lions.   _____

3. Sometimes the Greenpeacers use motor-driven rafts.   _____

4. Greenpeacers often protect mother whales from their calves.   _____

5. Once, an arrow came close to hitting a Greenpeace member.   _____

6. The members of Greenpeace are volunteers.   _____

7. Today, whalers hold their fire when they see a Greenpeace raft.   _____

8. Greenpeace was begun in the late 1930s.   _____

9. The Greenpeace Foundation was started by Canadians and Russians.   _____

10. There are over 250,000 Greenpeace members around the world.   _____

WHAT'S YOUR OPINION?

1. Would you risk your life to save an animal? Why or why not?

_____

_____

_____

_____

2. Greenpeacers have used dangerous methods such as risking their lives, and peaceful methods like handing out T-shirts. Which do you think is more effective? Why?

_____

_____

_____

_____

DEVELOPING SPELLING SKILLS

Study List

Singular	Plural
calf	calves
elf	elves
half	halves
hoof	hooves
knife	knives
leaf	leaves
life	lives
loaf	loaves
ourself	ourselves
shelf	shelves
thief	thieves
wharf	wharves
wife	wives
wolf	wolves
yourself	yourselves

Some words ending in *f*, like *sheriff*, form their plurals the regular way—by adding *s*. The plural of *sheriff* is *sheriffs*. However, some words that end in *f* or *fe* form their plurals irregularly.

Rule: Some words that end in *f* or *fe* form their plurals by dropping the *f* or *fe* and adding *ves*.

Examples:

Singular	Plural
life	lives
knife	knives
calf	calves

On your left is a Study List of words. Each word ends in *f* or *fe* in its singular form. All of these words form their plurals by dropping the final *f* or *fe* and adding *ves*. The words listed are almost all the words in English that form their plurals this way.

SKILL DRILL 1

Circle the final *f* or *fe* in each of the following words. Then write the plural form of the word on the line provided.

1. thief _____
2. ourself _____
3. loaf _____
4. elf _____
5. life _____
6. wolf _____
7. half _____

8. shelf _____
9. leaf _____
10. calf _____
11. yourself _____
12. hoof _____
13. knife _____
14. wife _____

15. wharf _____

SKILL DRILL 2

The following are short definitions of words from the Study List. The definitions are for the words in their singular form. Write the *singular form* of the Study List word that matches the definition. If you need help, check the Mini-Dictionary in the back of this book.

1. Bread shaped in one long piece _____

2. A wild animal somewhat like a dog _____

3. One who steals _____

4. A piece of wood that is fastened to a wall to hold things such as books _____

5. A cutting tool with a sharp edge _____

6. One of two equal parts _____

7. A married woman _____

8. A platform for loading and unloading ships _____

9. We or us _____

10. A thin, green part of a tree or plant _____

11. A tiny, mischievous character in fairy tales _____

12. You _____

13. The period of living _____

14. A hard covering on the feet of some animals _____

15. A young cow, bull, whale, or elephant _____

SKILL DRILL 3

Fill in each blank with the plural of the noun in parentheses to form a Study List word.

1. Please be sure to take care of (yourself) _____.

2. The calf's (hoof) _____ were stirring up the dust.

3. This bakery will sell (half) _____ of a cake.

4. Many hungry (wolf) _____ are roaming this forest.

5. There are plenty of empty (shelf) _____ in the closet.

6. The sharper (knife) _____ are in the drawer.

7. The workers will unload the ships down at the (wharf) _____.

8. We always enjoy (ourself) _____ at the picnic.

9. The trees are beginning to lose their (leaf) _____.

10. There are (elf) _____ living in the stump of that tree.

11. The members risk their (life) _____ to save the whales.

12. Three young (calf) _____ were running across the field.

13. The boys are making (loaf) _____ of bread.

14. People who shoplift are (thief) _____.

15. All of these women are (wife) _____ and mothers.

SKILL DRILL 4

Answer the following questions by using words from the Study List. You must write both the singular and plural forms of the word.

Singular	Plural

Which word has the vowel combination *ie*?

1. _____   _____

Which word has the vowel combination *ea*?

2. _____   _____

Which words contain the word *elf* in their singular form?

3. _____   _____

4. _____   _____

5. _____   _____

6. _____   _____

Singular	**Plural**

Which word contains the vowel combination *oa*?

7. _____   _____

Which word contains the vowel combination *oo*?

8. _____   _____

Which words end with *ife* in their singular form?

9. _____   _____

10. _____   _____

11. _____   _____

What word ends with *arf* in its singular form?

12. _____   _____

Which words end with *alf* in their singular form?

13. _____   _____

14. _____   _____

Which word ends with *olf* in its singular form?

15. _____   _____

Study List

Plural
calves
elves
halves
hooves
knives
leaves
lives
loaves
ourselves
shelves
thieves
wharves
wives
wolves
yourselves

WORD GAME 6

This is a puzzle without clues! Study the length and spelling of the plural form of each Study List word. Then figure out which words from the Study List fit in the spaces. Once you have found the first word, the rest will be easy to find. Remember to use the plural form of each word.

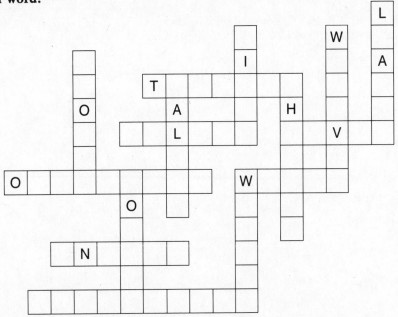

HOW WELL CAN YOU SPELL?

Try to take this practice test without looking back at **Lesson 6.** After you have finished, check your work against the Study List. Correct any mistakes you have made.

A. One word in each of the following pairs of words is spelled incorrectly. Circle that word and spell it correctly on the line provided.

1. elves, knifes   _____

2. lifes, yourself   _____

3. calves, wifes   _____

4. half, hoovs   _____

5. woolfs, loaves   _____

6. wharf, ourselfs   _____

7. shelvs, leaves   _____

8. thiefs, knife   _____

B. In each of the following sentences, one word is spelled incorrectly. Find that word. Then spell it correctly on the line provided.

9. Diane divided all of the pieces into halfs.   _____

10. There are several loafs of bread on the shelf.   _____

11. The car is parked down by the wharfs.   _____

12. Tom thinks that he's been seeing elfs.   _____

13. Please treat yourselfs to some milk and cookies.   _____

14. The mother whale is protecting her calfs.   _____

15. In summer, those trees are covered with leafs.   _____

Riches From the Deep

The year was 1641. Pirates roamed the Caribbean Sea off the coast of South America. Huge galleons, which are Spanish sailing vessels, sailed the seven seas. The Spanish ship, *Concepción*, was heavy with treasure on its way home. As it came near to the Florida coast, a fierce hurricane rose. The ship was helpless. Desperately, the crew cut loose sails and chopped off pieces of wood that held the sails. They were trying to keep the vessel afloat. But the *Concepción* was overturned.

While still hoping to hide the ship's treasure from the pirates, the captain made way for Puerto Rico. But 80 miles from shore, the ship hit a coral reef. Along with its precious cargo, the ship sank to the ocean floor.

Just 44 years later, the treasure was found. William Phips, an adventurer from Maine, was sent by the king of England to discover the remains of the sunken vessel. He hauled up 32 tons of silver from the wreck. Phips gave one fifth of his find to the king of England, who still ruled over America. Phips was then made governor of the Massachusetts Bay Colony.

But that was hardly the end of the *Concepción's* story. Three hundred years after the ship went down, an adventurer named Burt Webber decided to try to find it. Webber searched for a few months and found nothing. He was about to give up. Luckily, before he did, William Phips's record book was found in England. Webber and his crew set sail, closely following the directions in Phips's log. A short distance from where the ship went down, they began to find treasure.

Experts claimed that there might be as much as 40 million dollars worth of gold and silver in the ship's watery grave. ''It could go beyond one's wildest dreams,'' said Webber. It looked like his ship had finally come in!

REVIEWING YOUR READING

Circle the letter beside the word or phrase that best completes the sentence.

1. The *Concepción* was a
   a. Russian ship.
   b. Spanish ship.
   c. French ship.
   d. British ship.

2. The ship was helpless when it sailed into a
   a. tornado.
   b. snowstorm.
   c. hurricane.
   d. cyclone.

3. The captain of the *Concepción* sailed toward Puerto Rico to
   a. spend the gold.
   b. take a vacation.
   c. sink the ship.
   d. hide the treasure.

4. The *Concepción* sank off the coast of
   a. Puerto Rico.
   b. Spain.
   c. Maine.
   d. Florida.

5. William Phips hauled up 32 tons of
   a. copper.
   b. silver.
   c. tin.
   d. diamonds.

6. Phips gave one fifth of the treasure he found to the
   a. king of England.
   b. governor of Massachusetts.
   c. president of Spain.
   d. governor of Puerto Rico.

7. A captain's log is a
   a. record book.
   b. piece of wood.
   c. huge sail.
   d. galleon.

8. Webber and his crew found the remains of the *Concepción* by
   a. following a treasure map.
   b. following the directions in Phips's log.
   c. digging near Puerto Rico.
   d. asking pirates for directions.

FIGURING THE FACTS

Decide whether the following statements are true or false. Write *T* on the line if the statement is true. If the statement is false, cross out the incorrect word or phrase in the sentence. Then write the correct word or phrase on the line to make the statement true.

1. A *galleon* is a treasure. _____

2. To keep the *Concepción* afloat, the crew cut loose the sails. _____

3. The *Concepción* sank when it hit another ship. _____

4. William Phips was an adventurer from Spain. _____

5. Phips found the treasure two years after the *Concepción* sank. _____

6. Phips was made a knight by the king of England. _____

7. Phips was made governor of Maine. _____

8. Three hundred years after the ship went down, Webber tried to find it. _____

9. Webber finally found treasure near the spot where the *Titanic* sank. _____

10. There may be as much as 40 million dollars worth of treasure in the *Concepción's* watery grave. _____

WHAT'S YOUR OPINION?

1. William Phips was sent by the king of England to find the treasure. Do you think that it was worth Phips's while? Why?

_____
_____
_____
_____

2. William Phips's record book helped Webber find the remains of the *Concepción*. Do you think it is important to keep records? Why?

_____
_____
_____
_____

DEVELOPING SPELLING SKILLS

Study List

absolutely
accurately
certainly
cleverly
clumsily
coarsely
desperately
entirely
immediately
luckily
nearly
rapidly
recently
separately
wearily

An **adjective** is a word that describes something. Look at this sentence: The *clever* fox hid behind the tree. The word *clever* is an adjective because it describes the noun *fox*.

An **adverb** is a word that describes the action. Look at this sentence: The fox *cleverly* hid behind the tree. The word *cleverly* is an adverb because it describes how the fox hid.

Notice that the difference in spelling between the adjective *clever* and the adverb *cleverly* is the suffix *ly*.

Rule: **To change most adjectives to adverbs, simply add the suffix *ly*.**

Here are some adjectives and adverbs taken from the reading selection.

Examples:	*Adjectives*	*Adverbs*
	near	nearly
	clever	cleverly
	desperate	desperately
	lucky	luckily

Notice that all the adjectives simply add *ly* to form adverbs—except *lucky*. Do you remember why? The rule for words that end in *y* applies to this word. Here is the rule to refresh your memory.

Rule: **When a word ends in *y* preceded by a consonant, change the *y* to *i* before adding a suffix except *ing*.**

On your left is a Study List of words. Each word in the list is an adverb.

SKILL DRILL 1

Change each of the following adjectives to adverbs by adding the suffix *ly*. Be sure to remember the rule for adding suffixes to words that end with the letter *y*.

1. clever   _____
2. entire   _____
3. accurate   _____
4. clumsy   _____
5. weary   _____
6. certain   _____
7. near   _____

8. recent   _____
9. immediate   _____
10. coarse   _____
11. desperate   _____
12. absolute   _____
13. lucky   _____
14. separate   _____

15. rapid   _____

SKILL DRILL 2

The following are short definitions of words from the Study List. Fill the blanks with words from the Study List that match the definitions. If you need help, check the Mini-Dictionary in the back of this book.

1. Without any restrictions; completely   _____
2. Including all the parts   _____
3. Without delay; happening at once   _____
4. In a tired or worn-out way   _____
5. Divided into parts or groups; individually   _____
6. Having a good result by chance   _____
7. Almost; not quite   _____
8. Very swiftly or quickly   _____
9. Happening a short time ago   _____
10. In an awkward manner   _____
11. Correctly   _____
12. Quick in thinking; smart   _____
13. Without any doubt or question   _____
14. Roughly; harshly   _____
15. Reckless because one has lost hope   _____

SKILL DRILL 3

Fill in each blank with the adverb form of the adjective in parentheses to form a Study List word.

1. The hikers (desperate) _____ climbed to the top.

2. Please come to my office (immediate) _____.

3. (Lucky) _____, there was a police officer nearby.

4. The fire destroyed (near) _____ all the trees.

5. The stream is moving quite (rapid) _____.

6. We all went to the movies (recent) _____.

7. Please wash those glasses (separate) _____.

8. The workers (weary) _____ marched toward home.

9. She is (absolute) _____ the best tennis player here.

10. Add two cups of onions (coarse) _____ chopped.

11. There is (certain) _____ no doubt of his ability.

12. The fox (clever) _____ hid behind the trees.

13. Please be sure you have added the figures (accurate) _____.

14. The ship is made (entire) _____ of wood.

15. The clown (clumsy) _____ fell into the barrel.

Study List
absolutely
accurately
certainly
cleverly
clumsily
coarsely
desperately
entirely
immediately
luckily
nearly
rapidly
recently
separately
wearily

SKILL DRILL 4

Answer the following questions by using words from the Study List.

Which words contain the word *ate*?

1. _____   2. _____

3. _____   4. _____

Which word contains the word *oar*?

5. _____

Which words contain the word *ear*?

6. _____   7. _____

Which word contains the word *lute*?

8. _____

Which word ends with the letters *sily*?

9. _____

Which word contains the word *luck*?

10. _____

Which word contains the word *rapid*?

11. _____

Which word contains the word *certain*?

12. _____

Which word contains the word *cent*?

13. _____

Which word contains the word *tire*?

14. _____

Which word contains the word *ever*?

15. _____

WORD GAME 7

The words from the Study List are scrambled on the left. Unscramble each word and write it correctly in the spaces on the right. If you unscramble the words correctly, you will find the answer to the puzzle question by reading the shaded column downward. Write your answer on the line below.

PADRILY

SEDREAPETLY
LOSBAETULY
RATENCILY
CIKLULY
LECEVRLY
TRNECELY

RITEENLY
REANLY
PEASRTAELY
IWAERLY
ROESACLY
SIMCULLY
UCACARETLY
MIMIDETAELY

What do you call riches from the deep? _____

HOW WELL CAN YOU SPELL?

Try to take this practice test without looking back at Lesson 7. After you have finished, check your work against the Study List. Correct any mistakes you have made.

A. One word in each of the following pairs of words is spelled incorrectly. Circle that word and spell it correctly on the line provided.

1. certainlly, cleverly   _____

2. entirely, rapidley   _____

3. recently, luckly   _____

4. coarsly, clumsily   _____

5. absolutely, separatelly   _____

6. accuratly, nearly   _____

7. immediatelly, wearily   _____

8. luckily, desperatly   _____

B. In each of the following sentences, one word is spelled incorrectly. Find that word. Then spell it correctly on the line provided.

9. We recentley visited the Museum of Modern Art.   _____

10. Edgar clumsyly tripped over the carpet.   _____

11. Your answer is absolutly correct.   _____

12. The dog cleverley hid the bone in the yard.   _____

13. That shirt is made entireley of silk.   _____

14. There aren't nearley enough people present.   _____

15. The shoppers came weariley home from the market.   _____

Pearlie Mae

Although she had no formal training as a singer or actress, Pearl Bailey's career lasted over six decades. Two Presidents awarded her the title "Ambassador of Love to the Entire World." That's probably because she was a firm believer in giving. She was proud to proclaim, "If audiences take away a part of me each night, they're welcome."

Her introduction to show business came back in 1933. At age 15, Pearl entered the amateur night contest at a Philadelphia theater. She won the first prize—five dollars. But she also got a job to perform there for the next two weeks. Her second amateur contest was at the famous Apollo Theater in New York. She won that too. But from then it was nothing but hard work as a chorus girl in traveling shows. As her experience grew, so did her talent. Eventually, she began to sing solo. Pearl made her night club debut in the mid 1940s. She was a big success. Then there was no stopping her. Singing appearances led her to the stage, and later, film and television. Her remarkable talent took her all over the world.

In the late 1970s, Pearl received an honorary doctor's degree from a university. (An honorary degree is one given as an honor without the required courses.) "After I got it, I realized that it wasn't enough," Pearl said. "I wanted to do it right, to do it all." So she went back to school, working on her own degree. "I want to earn everything I get," she said. "I think that's important." So in her mid-sixties, Pearl got her degree.

In her autobiography, *Between You and Me*, she said, "I don't always have the kind of words I want to express myself." But she offered some advice to other students. She believed that there's one sure-fire way to get and do what you want. "If you want an education, read. If you can't travel, read, read, read."

Her friends called her Pearlie Mae. This Pearl was a gem.

58

REVIEWING YOUR READING

Circle the letter beside the word or phrase that best completes the sentence.

1. Pearl's introduction to show business came at age

   a. five.
   b. 50.
   c. 15.
   d. 65.

2. Her first performance was

   a. in an amateur contest.
   b. as a chorus girl.
   c. at the Apollo Theater.
   d. in a night club.

3. Pearl was appointed "Ambassador of Love" by

   a. the Queen of England.
   b. three American Ambassadors.
   c. a majority of voters.
   d. two American Presidents.

4. Pearl made her solo singing debut in the mid—

   a. 1920s.
   b. 1940s.
   c. 1970s.
   d. 1980s.

5. An honorary degree is one that

   a. is given after taking classes.
   b. doesn't mean anything.
   c. takes the place of a real degree.
   d. is given without the required courses.

6. Pearl went back to school because she wanted to

   a. earn a degree.
   b. study show business.
   c. meet intelligent people.
   d. teach others how to sing.

7. You can conclude that Pearl Bailey

   a. rarely earned what she got.
   b. had a difficult life.
   c. worked hard for what she had.
   d. was an instant success in show business.

8. Pearl believed that the one sure-fire way to get what you want is to

   a. become a singer.
   b. read as much as you can.
   c. write a book.
   d. enter amateur contests.

FIGURING THE FACTS

Decide whether the following statements are true or false. Write *T* on the line if the statement is true. Write *F* if the statement is false.

1. Pearl Bailey first performed in the 1930s. _____

2. Pearl won five dollars in her first amateur contest. _____

3. Pearl did not win her second amateur contest. _____

4. She worked as a chorus girl in traveling shows. _____

5. She has performed in film and television. _____

6. Pearl was awarded an honorary high school diploma. _____

7. Her autobiography is titled *Between You and Me*. _____

8. Pearl once performed at the Apollo Theater in New York. _____

9. Pearl's career lasted over eight decades. _____

10. Pearl earned a college degree when she was in her twenties. _____

WHAT'S YOUR OPINION?

1. What do you think Pearl meant when she said, "If audiences take away a part of me each night, they're welcome"?

_____

_____

_____

_____

_____

_____

2. Why do you think Pearl used to say, "If you can't travel, read"?

_____

_____

_____

_____

_____

_____

DEVELOPING SPELLING SKILLS

Study List

accidentally
actually
cheerfully
faithfully
finally
gracefully
initially
legally
locally
naturally
occasionally
practically
really
respectfully
totally

As you know, an **adjective** is a word that describes something. Look at this sentence: The *graceful* singer sang a tune. The word *graceful* is an adjective because it describes the noun *singer*.

An **adverb** is a word that describes the action. Look at this sentence: The singer *gracefully* sang a tune. The word *gracefully* describes how she sang the tune.

Notice that the difference between the adjective *graceful* and the adverb *gracefully* is the suffix *ly*.

Rule: **To change adjectives that end in *l* to adverbs, add the suffix *ly*.**

Examples:
Adjectives	*Adverbs*
accidental	accidentally
real	really
graceful	gracefully

On your left is a Study List of words. Each word in the list is an adverb.

SKILL DRILL 1

Change the following adjectives to adverbs by adding the suffix *ly*.

1. respectful _____
2. accidental _____
3. occasional _____
4. real _____
5. cheerful _____
6. final _____
7. initial _____

8. total _____
9. natural _____
10. practical _____
11. actual _____
12. faithful _____
13. graceful _____
14. legal _____

15. local _____

SKILL DRILL 2

The following are short definitions of words from the Study List. Fill the blanks with words from the Study List that match the definitions. If you need help, check the Mini-Dictionary in the back of this book.

1. Almost or nearly _____
2. Truly or actually _____
3. Really or in fact _____
4. Done with joy or gladness _____
5. Loyally; honestly _____
6. Last; coming at the end _____
7. First; coming at the beginning _____
8. Beautifully and smoothly _____
9. Allowed by law; lawfully _____
10. Feeling or showing respect _____
11. Completely; entirely; in a total manner _____
12. Mistakenly; unexpectedly; happening by mistake _____
13. In a natural way; as one might expect _____
14. Once in awhile; now and then _____
15. Within a particular place; nearby _____

SKILL DRILL 3

Answer the following questions by using words from the Study List.

Which word contains the word *tot*?

1. _____

Which word contains the word *occasion*?

2. _____

Which word contains the word *accident*?

3. _____

Which words contain the word *act*?

4. _____   5. _____

Which words contain the word *fully*?

6. _____   7. _____

8. _____   9. _____

Which word contains the word *leg*?

10. _____

Which word contains the word *real*?

11. _____

Which words contain the word *natural*?

12. _____

Which word contains the word *local*?

14. _____

Which word contains the word *fin*?

13. _____

Which word contains the word *initial*?

15. _____

Study List
accidentally
actually
cheerfully
faithfully
finally
gracefully
initially
legally
locally
naturally
occasionally
practically
really
respectfully
totally

SKILL DRILL 4

Fill in each blank with the adverb form of the adjective in parentheses to form a Study List word.

1. The storm did damage (local) _____.

2. We (occasional) _____ go to that restaurant.

3. All of these vegetables are grown (natural) _____.

4. James (accidental) _____ broke the mirror.

5. The thief was not (total) _____ honest about the crime.

6. The gentleman (respectful) _____ took off his hat.

7. Please cross the street (legal) _____.

8. The dancers (graceful) _____ waltzed across the floor.

9. The letter (final) _____ arrived today.

10. My alarm clock rings (faithful) _____ at eight.

11. The children (cheerful) _____ greeted the ambassador.

12. Jane is (real) _____ leaving this afternoon.

13. That picture was (initial) _____ at the front of the book.

14. There is (practical) _____ no mustard left.

15. She is (actual) _____ Margo's twin sister.

WORD GAME 8

The words in the Study List are used in this puzzle. The numbers of the clues match the numbers in the puzzle. Read the clues below. Then write your answers in the puzzle blocks.

ACROSS

4. Synonym for *really*
6. At the beginning
7. In a total manner
10. Coming at the end
12. In a natural way
13. Nearby
14. Synonym for *actually*
15. Showing respect

DOWN

1. By mistake
2. Loyally; deserving trust
3. Almost or nearly
5. Done with joy
8. Once in awhile
9. Done with grace or beauty
11. Allowed by law

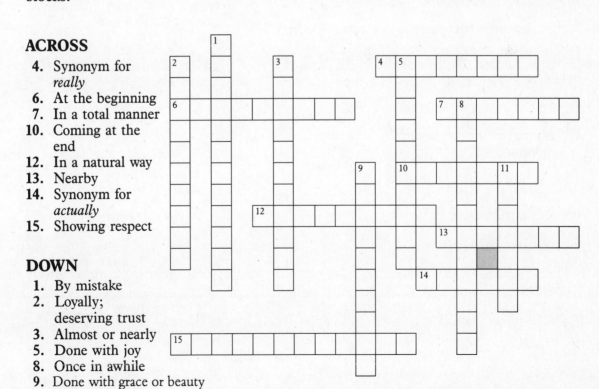

HOW WELL CAN YOU SPELL?

Try to take this practice test without looking back at Lesson 8. After you have finished, check your work against the Study List. Correct any mistakes you have made.

A. One word in each of the following pairs of words is spelled incorrectly. Circle that word and spell it correctly on the line provided.

1. faithfuly, finally   _____

2. really, localy   _____

3. totaly, gracefully   _____

4. initialy, cheerfully   _____

5. actually, legaly   _____

6. occasionally, naturaly   _____

7. respectfuly, accidentally   _____

B. In each of the following sentences, one word is spelled incorrectly. Find that word. Then spell it correctly on the line provided.

8. Ellen is actualy the first person on the list.   _____

9. The family occasionaly goes to the park together.   _____

10. We accidentaly took the wrong turn.   _____

11. He arrived when dinner was practicaly over.   _____

12. Finaly, the train slowly approached the station.   _____

13. This is realy the first time I've been on skates.   _____

14. Dorothy gracefuly turned on the ice.   _____

15. Mr. Johnson cheerfuly greets his students each
    morning.   _____

9

The Dinner Party

It took almost five years to set the table. But the "guests" will never sit down to eat because it's not a real dinner party. It's a work of art. The creation is a combination of sculpture, painting, and needlework. It is called "The Dinner Party," and it is dedicated to all the women of the world.

"The Dinner Party" stands in the center of a room at San Francisco's Museum of Modern Art. The main piece is a huge, triangular-shaped table. This object was chosen partly because the triangle has been a symbol for women throughout history. Also, in the past, women have been known as preparers of the family table.

There are 39 settings of silverware and china. Each place is for a famous woman in history. Each has a different handmade plate, tableware, and a drinking goblet. At each place is a linen mat on which the famous woman's name is sewn. Also hand-stitched on the mat are some pictures and symbols that show the life of the famous "guest."

The huge table rests on a floor made of triangular clay tiles. Nine hundred and ninety-nine women's names are written on these tiles. All of the names are important in world history.

The project was the idea of artist Judy Chicago. For the first two years, Judy worked alone on the creation. Slowly, others grew interested and began to offer their help. More than 400 people worked on the masterpiece, which took almost five years to complete. Their work is a celebration of women in art and history. And there couldn't be a better place to celebrate than at a dinner party!

REVIEWING YOUR READING

Circle the letter beside the word or phrase that best completes the sentence.

1. "The Dinner Party" is a

   a. picture.
   b. piece of music.
   c. work of art.
   d. meal.

2. "The Dinner Party" is dedicated to all the

   a. people of the world.
   b. women of the world.
   c. men of the world.
   d. children of the world.

3. The main piece in "The Dinner Party" is a

   a. square table.
   b. round table.
   c. triangular-shaped table.
   d. rectangular-shaped table.

4. At the table there are

   a. 39 people.
   b. 39 place settings.
   c. 93 people.
   d. 93 place settings.

5. The triangle is an ancient symbol for

   a. women.
   b. art.
   c. dinner.
   d. sculpture.

6. Each place setting has a hand-stitched

   a. plate.
   b. knife.
   c. mat.
   d. napkin.

7. The word *stitched* means

   a. drawn.
   b. sewn.
   c. painted.
   d. cooked.

8. For the first two years, Judy Chicago worked on "The Dinner Party"

   a. alone.
   b. with 88 other people.
   c. only at night.
   d. with three other people.

FIGURING THE FACTS

Decide whether the following statements are true or false. Write *T* on the line if the statement is true. If the statement is false, cross out the incorrect word or phrase in the sentence. Then write the correct word or phrase on the line to make the statement true.

1. It took almost ten years to create "The Dinner Party."

2. "The Dinner Party" is a combination of sculpture, needlework, and music.

3. "The Dinner Party" celebrates women in history.

4. In the past, women have been known as preparers of the table.

5. Each setting at the table is dedicated to a real woman in history.

6. The plates on the table were made by hand.

7. There is a plastic mat at each place on the table.

8. A drinking goblet is a type of a cup.

9. The table rests on a floor made of clay tiles.

10. The tiles are in the shape of squares.

WHAT'S YOUR OPINION?

1. In the past, women have been known as preparers of the table. Why do you think this was the case? How have things changed?

2. In what ways is the table of "The Dinner Party" different from other dinner tables? What do you think makes Judy Chicago's table a work of art?

DEVELOPING SPELLING SKILLS

Study List

artist's
couldn't
doesn't
haven't
it's
mechanic's
passenger's
secretary's
shouldn't
we'll
where's
women's
won't
wouldn't
you've

There are two major uses of the **apostrophe** that you should know.

Rule: **The apostrophe is used to show possession.**

Example: The artist's painting

The painting is owned by the artist. Therefore, we use the apostrophe followed by the letter *s* to show possession.

Example: Women's names

The names belong to the *women*. Therefore, we again use the apostrophe followed by the letter *s* to show possession.

Rule: **The apostrophe is used to show that a letter or letters have been omitted.**

Example: **Couldn't** is a short form of **could not**.

Could and *not* have been joined together and the second *o* has been omitted. The place for the missing letter is being held by the apostrophe.

Example: **Won't** is a short form of **will not**.

Will and *not* have been joined together and the space for the missing letters is held open by the apostrophe.

Words like *couldn't* and *won't* are called **contractions** because they shorten or contract two words.

On your left is a Study List of words. Each demonstrates use of the apostrophe. Remember, there are two major uses of the apostrophe: to show possession or to replace a missing letter.

SKILL DRILL 1

Each of the following words is missing an apostrophe. Rewrite each word with the apostrophe in its proper place.

1. shouldnt   _____
2. secretarys   _____
3. its   _____
4. passengers   _____
5. wouldnt   _____
6. womens   _____
7. wheres   _____

8. couldnt   _____
9. doesnt   _____
10. mechanics   _____
11. artists   _____
12. wont   _____
13. havent   _____
14. well   _____

15. youve   _____

SKILL DRILL 2

The following are short definitions of words from the Study List. Fill the blanks with words from the Study List that match the definitions. If you need help, check the Mini-Dictionary in the back of this book.

1. Belonging to the mechanic   _____
2. Belonging to the passenger   _____
3. Could not   _____
4. Have not   _____
5. Belonging to the artist   _____
6. Will not   _____
7. Belonging to the women   _____
8. Should not   _____
9. Belonging to the secretary   _____
10. Does not   _____
11. It is   _____
12. Would not   _____
13. Where is   _____
14. We will   _____
15. You have   _____

SKILL DRILL 3

Change the words in parentheses to possessives or contractions and rewrite the sentence on the line provided. The first one is done for you.

1. The studio (of the artist) contains many beautiful paintings.

    The artist's studio contains many beautiful paintings.

2. The tools (of the mechanic) are in the bag.

   _____

3. Tom (could not) attend the class picnic.

   _____

4. The luggage (of the passenger) is on the train.

   _____

5. I (have not) been to the library for two days.

   _____

6. Sandra (will not) be taking the bus today.

   _____

7. The paintings (of the women) will be on display tonight.

   _____

8. A person (should not) go swimming after eating a big meal.

   _____

9. The desk (of the secretary) is in the corner.

   _____

10. The whole trip (does not) take more than three hours.

   _____

11. (It is) ten minutes past four o'clock.

   _____

12. (You have) stored plenty of food in the refrigerator.

   _____

13. I (would not) do that if I were you.

   _____

14. (Where is) the vacuum cleaner?

   _____

15. We're going away, but (we will) be right back.

   _____

SKILL DRILL 4

Answer the following questions by using words from the Study List.

Which words are possessives?

1. _____   2. _____

3. _____   4. _____

5. _____

Which contractions contain an apostrophe in place of the letter *i*?

6. _____   7. _____

Which contraction contains an apostrophe in place of the letters *wi*?

8. _____

Which contractions contain an apostrophe in place of the letter *o*?

9. _____   10. _____

11. _____   12. _____

13. _____   14. _____

Which contraction contains an apostrophe in place of the letters *ha*?

15. _____

Study List

artist's
couldn't
doesn't
haven't
it's
mechanic's
passenger's
secretary's
shouldn't
we'll
where's
women's
won't
wouldn't
you've

WORD GAME 9

All of the letters from the words in the Study List appear in this puzzle. Cross out the letters of the puzzle as you use them to spell the Study List words. There will be enough letters left to answer the question below.

```
                  A
               A  A  A
            A  C  C  C  C
         D  D  D  D  D  E  E
         E  E  E  E  E  E  E  E  E
      E  F  G  H  H  H  H  I  I  I  L
   L  L  L  L  M  M  N  N  N  N  N  N  N  N
   O  O  O  O  O  O  O  O  P  R  R  R  R  R
      S  S  S  S  S  S  S  S  S  S  S
         S  S  T  T  T  T  T  T
            T  T  T  U  U  U  U
               V  V  W  W  W
                  W  W  Y
                     Y
```

What was missing at the "Dinner Party"?

_____

HOW WELL CAN YOU SPELL?

Try to take this practice test without looking back at Lesson 9. After you have finished, check your work against the Study List. Correct any mistakes you have made.

A. One word in each of the following pairs of words is spelled incorrectly. Circle that word and spell it correctly on the line provided. Be careful: a word is spelled incorrectly if an apostrophe is missing or out of place.

1. coul'dnt, wouldn't   _____

2. doe'snt, artist's   _____

3. secretary's, wel'l   _____

4. shoul'dnt, women's   _____

5. passenger's, hav'nt   _____

6. yo've, mechanic's   _____

7. i'ts, won't   _____

B. In each of the following sentences, one word is spelled incorrectly. Find that word. Then spell it correctly on the line provided.

8. There is a flat tire on the mechanics truck.   _____

9. We wont be taking the train to work today.   _____

10. Wheres the flower pot that was on the shelf?   _____

11. Diane will be playing on the womens team.   _____

12. The secretarys note pad is sitting on the desk.   _____

13. The painting is displayed in the artists studio.   _____

14. Please take that passenge'rs ticket.   _____

15. The extra dishes woul'dnt fit into the cupboard.   _____

True Colors

"Crayons aren't just for kids anymore!" At least, that's what the people at Binney & Smith say. They're the makers of Crayolas, the world's most famous crayons. Over two billion Crayolas are sold every year. That many crayons laid end to end could circle the globe five times!

We usually associate crayons with grade school. But today, adults are using crayons to express themselves. It seems that more artists are using crayons. Designers are using them. There are even restaurants that supply you with crayons and paper. That's so you can doodle while you wait for your food.

In a lifetime, an average person will wear down seven hundred crayons. That's almost a dozen boxes. And those are the big boxes, the ones with the built-in sharpener on the side! (A sharp crayon is essential to good drawing.)

But what about the lifetime of a crayon? A single crayon can be created in about three to five minutes. Binney & Smith tells us that most people use a crayon only halfway down. Then they get thrown away. The most popular colors, however, do seem to stay around a little longer. Of course, we're referring to red and black.

Everyone knows what plum and peach look like. But exactly what color is periwinkle? Or for that matter, what is cornflower? If you are guessing that they are shades of blue, you're right! But who names all those colors? For Crayola, things are done strictly by the book. The book is "Color: Universal Language and Dictionary of Names." It is published by the U.S. Government. And it contains precise guides to hundreds of different shades. Eight fluorescent colors were added to Crayola's rainbow in the 1970s. Otherwise, the colors haven't changed in the 90 years of Crayola history.

The box top says "Non-Toxic." That means you won't die if you decide to eat your crayons while you're waiting for your dinner to arrive.

REVIEWING YOUR READING

Circle the letter beside the word or phrase that best completes the sentence.

1. If all the Crayolas sold in one year were laid end to end, they could

   a. circle the earth 50 times.
   b. reach the moon and back.
   c. circle the earth five times.
   d. circle the moon five times.

2. In one lifetime, an average person uses up

   a. one box of crayons.
   b. one dozen crayons.
   c. twelve dozen crayons.
   d. a dozen boxes of crayons.

3. The most popular colors of crayons are

   a. blue and red.
   b. red and black.
   c. red and green.
   d. green and blue.

4. A crayon can be made in as little as

   a. one to three minutes.
   b. two to five minutes.
   c. three to five minutes.
   d. five to eight minutes.

5. "Color: Universal Language and Dictionary of Names" is a book of

   a. different color shades.
   b. various types of crayons.
   c. government artists.
   d. drawings made with crayons.

6. We usually associate crayons with grade school. In this sentence the word *associate* probably means

   a. think of.
   b. colors.
   c. partners.
   d. use.

7. It contains precise guides to hundreds of different shades. In this sentence, the word *precise* probably means

   a. pretty near.
   b. exact.
   c. different.
   d. pretty good.

8. *Non-toxic* means

   a. poisonous.
   b. edible.
   c. not poisonous.
   d. not edible.

FIGURING THE FACTS

Decide whether the following statements are true or false. Write *T* on the line if the statement is true. If the statement is false, cross out the incorrect word or phrase in the sentence. Then write the correct word or phrase on the line to make the statement true.

1. The makers of Crayolas are Binney & Smith.   _____

2. We usually associate crayons with high school.   _____

3. Some restaurants are giving customers crayons.   _____

4. The big boxes of Crayolas do not have a sharpener.   _____

5. Most people use the whole crayon.   _____

6. Over two billion Crayolas are sold every year.   _____

7. Cornflower is a shade of blue.   _____

8. Peach and plum are Crayola color names.   _____

9. Crayolas are the world's most famous crayons.   _____

10. Periwinkle is a shade of green.   _____

WHAT'S YOUR OPINION?

1. Why do you think people only use half of their crayons? Do you think that this is wasteful? Why?

_____

_____

_____

_____

_____

_____

2. Some psychologists say that doodling can help you to express your inner feelings. Do you think this is true? Why or why not?

_____

_____

_____

_____

_____

_____

DEVELOPING SPELLING SKILLS

Study List

associate
autobiography
avoid
biscuit
bouquet
career
committee
essential
guessing
optional
pursuit
recruit
superior
theater
understood

The following words appear in the reading selection.

associate   guessing   essential

Each of these words contains two vowels together. We don't always hear all of the sounds in words. Sometimes the vowels come together to make one sound like the *ue* in guessing. But notice that the *i* and *a* in associate are sounded separately.

On your left is a Study List of words. Each of these contains two vowels in combination with each other. Be extra careful when spelling these words.

SKILL DRILL 1

Rewrite each of the following words on the lines provided. Then circle the vowel combinations in each.

1. bouquet _____   8. career _____
2. optional _____   9. pursuit _____
3. recruit _____   10. superior _____
4. theater _____   11. understood _____
5. associate _____   12. autobiography _____
6. avoid _____   13. biscuit _____
7. committee _____   14. essential _____

15. guessing _____

SKILL DRILL 2

The following are short definitions of words from the Study List. Fill the blanks with words from the Study List that match the definitions. If you need help, check the Mini-Dictionary in the back of this book.

1. Forming an opinion without really knowing _____
2. A bunch of flowers _____
3. A place where plays are acted _____
4. Necessary; needed to make a thing what it is _____
5. To have learned the meaning of something _____
6. To join or connect with something _____
7. The story of a person's life written by him or her _____
8. To keep away from _____
9. A job or course of progress through life _____
10. Not required; left to one's own choice _____
11. The act of pursuing or following _____
12. To get new members _____
13. Very good or above average _____
14. A group of persons appointed to do certain things _____
15. A small, soft bread-like cake _____

SKILL DRILL 3

The vowels are missing from each of the following words. First, fill the blanks with vowels to form words from the Study List. Then write the words you have formed on the lines provided.

1. und _ rst _ _ d   _____
2. _ ss _ c _ _ t _   _____
3. c _ r _ _ r   _____
4. _ pt _ _ n _ l   _____
5. p _ rs _ _ t   _____
6. _ ss _ nt _ _ l   _____
7. _ _ t _ b _ _ gr _ phy   _____
8. _ v _ _ d   _____
9. g _ _ ss _ ng   _____
10. b _ _ q _ _ t   _____
11. th _ _ t _ r   _____
12. r _ cr _ _ t   _____
13. s _ p _ r _ _ r   _____
14. c _ mm _ tt _ _   _____
15. b _ sc _ _ t   _____

Study List

associate
autobiography
avoid
biscuit
bouquet
career
committee
essential
guessing
optional
pursuit
recruit
superior
theater
understood

SKILL DRILL 4

Answer the following questions by using words from the Study List.

Which words contain the vowel combination *ee*?

1. _____   2. _____

Which word contains the combination *oo*?

3. _____

Which words contain the vowel combination *io*?

4. _____   5. _____

6. _____

Which word contains the vowel combination *oi*?

7. _____

Which words contain the vowel combination *ia*?

8. _____   9. _____

Which word contains the vowel combination *ea*?

10. _____

Which words contain the vowel combination *ui*?

11. _____   12. _____

13. _____

Which words contain the vowel combination *ue*?

14. _____   15. _____

WORD GAME 10

The words from the Study List are used in this puzzle. The numbers of the clues match the numbers in the puzzle.

ACROSS

3. Not required
5. Place for plays
6. Connect with something
8. Necessary
10. Get new members
12. A job
13. Stay away
14. Bunch of flowers

DOWN

1. Forming an opinion without knowing
2. A group appointed to do something
4. Above average
6. A person's own life story
7. Knew the meaning of something
9. A small cake
11. The act of pursuing

HOW WELL CAN YOU SPELL?

Try to take this practice test without looking back at Lesson 10. After you have finished, check your work against the Study List. Correct any mistakes you have made.

A. One word in each of the following pairs of words is spelled incorrectly. Circle that word and spell it correctly on the line provided.

1. understod, guessing   _____

2. bouquet, avoyd   _____

3. comittie, pursuit   _____

4. recruit, carear   _____

5. superrear, biscuit   _____

6. essential, autobiagraphy   _____

7. optshunal, associate   _____

B. In each of the following sentences, one word is spelled incorrectly. Find that word. Then spell it correctly on the line provided.

8. The play will be performed in the school theeter.   _____

9. The army would like to recroot more women.   _____

10. Be sure to try a biskit with your meal.   _____

11. Brushing is essenchal to good dental care.   _____

12. The older students will not assoseate with club members.   _____

13. Gessing the answers will not help you to pass the test.   _____

14. The winner was presented with a boquet of roses.   _____

15. Everyone is entitled to life, liberty, and the persoot of happiness.   _____

Ships of the Desert

Some are seven or eight feet tall. They weigh as much as half a ton. They are humpbacked, knock-kneed, and flat-footed. They'll eat almost anything, even bushes, thorns, and leaves. In a moment of hunger, they've been known to eat the straw roof off a desert hut! People may chuckle at these awkward creatures. But camels always have the last laugh.

For people who live in desert areas, camels are the most valuable animals in the world. They are a serious means of transportation. In fact, they are called "ships of the desert." It is a well-earned name. Camels can travel for two or three days without water. When they do drink, they gulp down as much as a bathtub full of water. They are also able to carry up to twice their own weight. And, camels don't get stuck in the sand like cars and trucks do. Best of all, they don't use gasoline!

When it comes to riding, camels are not always eager to cooperate. First you must get the camel to kneel. Then you approach from the rear and scramble aboard, before the camel starts to rise. Once on, the trick is to stay on. When the camel moves, the rider bobs from side to side, and up and down. As in riding a roller coaster, the secret is to hold on tight.

Countless lives have been saved by the strength and endurance of camels. Recently, there was a drought in Central Africa. Thousands of people were in danger of starving. Camels saved the day. They transported 5,000 tons of food through the desert to the helpless people.

But camels aren't used only for transportation. Each year in Saudi Arabia, thousands of people flock to watch the camel races. The sight is something to behold. One hundred camels gallop across the desert, as riders gracefully balance themselves on the humps.

REVIEWING YOUR READING

Circle the letter beside the word or phrase that best completes the sentence.

1. Camels have been known to eat

   a. tin roofs.
   b. straw roofs.
   c. brick buildings.
   d. glass.

2. In desert countries, camels are called

   a. ships of the desert.
   b. ships of the sea.
   c. trucks of the desert.
   d. horses of the desert.

3. Camels can travel without water for

   a. two or three days.
   b. five or six days.
   c. seven or eight days.
   d. nine or ten days.

4. In order to ride a camel, first you must

   a. get the animal to sit.
   b. get the animal to kneel.
   c. make the animal gallop.
   d. make the animal trot.

5. According to the story, you can conclude that riding a camel is

   a. safe.
   b. smooth.
   c. difficult.
   d. easy.

6. Other than transportation, camels are used for

   a. racing.
   b. food.
   c. digging sand.
   d. finding water.

7. During a drought in Central Africa, camels transported 5,000

   a. tons of food.
   b. tons of water.
   c. people.
   d. desert huts.

8. According to the story, you can conclude that in desert nations camels

   a. are not needed.
   b. do more harm than good.
   c. often get stuck in sand.
   d. are very valuable.

FIGURING THE FACTS

Decide whether the following statements are true or false. Write *T* on the line if the statement is true. If the statement is false, cross out the incorrect word or phrase in the sentence. Then write the correct word or phrase on the line to make the statement true.

1. Some camels are seven or eight feet tall. _____

2. Some camels weigh as much as eight tons. _____

3. Camels will eat almost anything. _____

4. Camels are not a means of transportation. _____

5. Camels won't drink more than a cup of water at a time. _____

6. Camels can carry up to six times their own weight. _____

7. Camels get stuck in sand. _____

8. Camels are always eager to carry riders. _____

9. A camel rider bobs up and down, and from side to side. _____

10. In Saudi Arabia, there are camel races. _____

WHAT'S YOUR OPINION?

1. Do you think camels could be a means of transportation where you live? Why or why not?

_____

_____

_____

_____

_____

2. The reading selection tells us that "camels always have the last laugh." What do you think the author means by this?

_____

_____

_____

_____

DEVELOPING SPELLING SKILLS

Study List

ambitious
approach
caution
cooperate
counterfeit
individual
lieutenant
manual
nervous
proclaim
realize
reliable
serious
vacuum
valuable

The following words appear in the reading selection.

approach   serious   cooperate

Each of these words has two or more vowels together. Since we don't always hear all the sounds in words, it is most important to know how to spell words with multiple vowels like those above. As you read through the Study List words, notice the silent vowels in each word.

On your left is a Study List of words. Each of these words contains two or more vowels in combination with each other. Be extra careful when spelling these words.

SKILL DRILL 1

Rewrite each of the following words on the lines provided. Then circle the multiple vowels in each.

1. serious _____
2. valuable _____
3. realize _____
4. nervous _____
5. ambitious _____
6. cooperate _____
7. counterfeit _____

8. vacuum _____
9. reliable _____
10. proclaim _____
11. manual _____
12. approach _____
13. caution _____
14. individual _____

15. lieutenant _____

SKILL DRILL 2

The following are short definitions of words from the Study List. Fill the blanks with words from the Study List that match the definitions. If you need help, check the Mini-Dictionary in the back of this book.

1. An empty space without any air in it _____
2. Showing a strong desire for fame or honor _____
3. To come near or nearer something _____
4. To warn or advise _____
5. Declare or make known publicly _____
6. To understand clearly _____
7. Dependable; worthy of trust _____
8. Important; grave _____
9. An army officer _____
10. Done with the hands _____
11. Restless or uneasy _____
12. Unite and work together _____
13. Not real; an illegal copy _____
14. One single person _____
15. Having value; being worth something _____

SKILL DRILL 3

The vowels are missing from each of the following words. First, fill the blanks with vowels to form words from the Study List. Then write the words you have formed on the lines provided.

1. m _ n _ _ l   _____

2. v _ l _ _ ble   _____

3. ind _ v _ d _ _ l   _____

4. amb _ t _ _ _ s   _____

5. s _ r _ _ _ s   _____

6. c _ _ t _ _ n   _____

7. c _ _ p _ r _ t _   _____

8. v _ c _ _ m   _____

9. r _ _ l _ z _   _____

10. pr _ cl _ _ m   _____

11. r _ l _ _ ble   _____

12. l _ _ _ t _ nant   _____

13. _ ppr _ _ ch   _____

14. c _ _ nterf _ _ t   _____

15. n _ rv _ _ s   _____

Study List
ambitious
approach
caution
cooperate
counterfeit
individual
lieutenant
manual
nervous
proclaim
realize
reliable
serious
vacuum
valuable

SKILL DRILL 4

Answer the following questions by using words from the Study List.

Which words contain the vowel combination *ua*?

1. _____   2. _____

3. _____

Which word contains the vowel combination *ai*?

4. _____

Which word contains the vowel combination *ia*?

5. _____

Which word contains the vowel combination *ieu*?

6. _____

Which word contains the vowel combination *oa*?

7. _____

Which words contain the vowel combination *ou*?

8. _____   9. _____

10. _____   11. _____

Which word contains the vowel combination *au*?

12. _____

Which word contains the vowel combination *oo*?

13. _____

Which word contains the vowel combination *uu*?

14. _____

Which word contains the vowel combination *ea*?

15. _____

WORD GAME 11

All of the letters from the words in the Study List appear in this puzzle. Cross out the letters of the puzzle as you use them to spell the Study List words. There will be enough letters left to answer the question below.

```
          A A A
        A A A A A
      A A A A A A A
      B B B C C C C C C
      D D E E E E E E E E E
    E E E E F H H I I I I I I
  I I I I I I L L L L L L L L L
  M M M M M N N N N N N O O O
    O O O O O O P P P P P R R
      R R R R R R S S S S S
        T T T T T T T U U
          U U U U U U U
            U U U V V
              V V Z
```

What do camels have that other animals do not? _____

HOW WELL CAN YOU SPELL?

Try to take this practice test without looking back at Lesson 11. After you have finished, check your work against the Study List. Correct any mistakes you have made.

A. One word in each of the following pairs of words is spelled incorrectly. Circle that word and spell it correctly on the line provided.

1. proclame, cooperate   _____

2. serious, realice   _____

3. individual, vacume   _____

4. aproach, valuable   _____

5. nervous, manuale   _____

6. ambitous, counterfeit   _____

7. lutenant, reliable   _____

8. caushun, proclaim   _____

B. In each of the following sentences, one word is spelled incorrectly. Find that word. Then spell it correctly on the line provided.

9. The accident taught Joanne a valueable lesson.   _____

10. The performers were nerveous before the curtain went up.   _____

11. Those ten-dollar bills are counterfit.   _____

12. Pete is the most relyable student in the class.   _____

13. Please coperate with the police during this emergency.   _____

14. Dinah is a talented individule.   _____

15. Hunger is a serius problem in most countries.   _____

Free Wheeling

They use no gas. They don't pollute. They're great for exercise, as well as transportation. And with a little practice, anyone can ride one. In case you haven't already guessed, this machine is the bicycle!

Bikes haven't always been easy to use. The first one was invented in 1690, and looked more like a scooter. It had two wheels and a board that was pushed around with the feet. This bike traveled in a straight line because there was no way to steer it. Doctors were quick to criticize the invention. They warned that it was harmful to people's health. It seems that all the pushing was hurting people's legs.

To solve the medical problem, someone invented pedals. Actually, these pedals were cranks. But they weren't pushed by the feet. Riders had to lie on the frame of the bike and turn the cranks with their hands! No one is sure exactly what this did to people's hands. Nevertheless, the bicycle industry continued to grow.

In those days, bicycles came in all sorts of shapes and sizes. Some had large rear wheels and small front ones, while others had just the opposite. But the great-granddaddy of the bicycle, as we know it today, was built in 1885. This cycle had two equal-sized wheels and it had a chain. It was called "The Rover," and was very popular.

Cycling was a big hit in the late 1800s. People did all sorts of crazy things on bikes. A man named Tom Stevens rode his bike around the world. It took him two years to complete the trip. That was pretty good time, considering that in many countries there were no roads.

With the invention of the automobile, the bicycle's popularity died down. Today bikes are coasting to a comeback. Let's hear it for pedal power!

REVIEWING YOUR READING

Circle the letter beside the word or phrase that best completes the sentence.

1. Bicycles

   a. pollute the air.
   b. use gasoline.
   c. provide no exercise.
   d. are a source of transportation.

2. The first bicycle looked like

   a. a roller skate.
   b. a scooter.
   c. a wagon.
   d. an automobile.

3. The first bicycle was known to hurt people's

   a. fingers.
   b. heads.
   c. legs.
   d. arms.

4. Some early bicycles had

   a. two front wheels.
   b. three rear wheels.
   c. large rear wheels.
   d. four small rear wheels.

5. The first bike, as we know it today, was called the

   a. tricycle.
   b. unicycle.
   c. "Rover."
   d. clover.

6. Cycling was very popular in the late

   a. 1300s.
   b. 1500s.
   c. 1600s.
   d. 1800s.

7. A man named Tom Stevens

   a. rode his bike around the world.
   b. invented a motor-driven bike.
   c. invented a chain-driven bike.
   d. rode his bike to the North Pole.

8. According to the story, you can conclude that

   a. bicycles replaced autos as transportation.
   b. bicycles are harmful to your health.
   c. automobiles replaced bicycles as transportation.
   d. automobiles are driven by chains.

FIGURING THE FACTS

Decide whether the following statements are true or false. Write *T* on the line if the statement is true. If the statement is false, cross out the incorrect word or phrase in the sentence. Then write the correct word or phrase on the line to make the statement true.

1. With a little practice, almost anyone can ride a bike. _____

2. Bicycles run on electric power. _____

3. The first bike was invented in 1960. _____

4. The first bike was pushed by the feet. _____

5. The first bike only traveled in a straight line. _____

6. On one type of bike, the rider had to lie down. _____

7. Some bikes had large rear wheels. _____

8. "The Rover" was invented in 1885. _____

9. "The Rover" was a motor-driven bicycle. _____

10. It took Tom Stevens ten years to ride around the world. _____

WHAT'S YOUR OPINION?

1. Why do you think the automobile took the place of the bicycle as a means of transportation?

_____

_____

_____

_____

_____

2. Do you think that bicycles are the answer to today's transportation problems? Why or why not?

_____

_____

_____

_____

_____

_____

DEVELOPING SPELLING SKILLS

Study List

accomplice
advertise
apprentice
criticize
disguise
exercise
improvise
itemize
patronize
practice
prejudice
revise
splice
standardize
summarize

The following words appear in the reading selection.

exercise   practice   criticize

Because the endings of these words look and sound somewhat alike, the endings are often confused. When learning the words in this chapter, it is most important to pay close attention to the endings in each word.

On your left is a Study List of words. Each word ends in either *ise, ice,* or *ize.* Be careful of the endings when you memorize these words!

SKILL DRILL 1

Rewrite each of the following words on the lines provided. Then circle the *ise, ize,* or *ice* ending in each.

1. prejudice _____
2. patronize _____
3. standardize _____
4. disguise _____
5. improvise _____
6. apprentice _____
7. summarize _____

8. practice _____
9. itemize _____
10. accomplice _____
11. criticize _____
12. exercise _____
13. advertise _____
14. splice _____

15. revise _____

SKILL DRILL 2

The following are short definitions of words from the Study List. Fill in the blanks with words from the Study List that match the definitions. If you need help, check the Mini-Dictionary in the back of this book.

1. To make something up as you go along _____
2. Activity that improves the body _____
3. A person learning a trade or art _____
4. To give public notice in a newspaper or on TV, etc. _____
5. To make a summary of _____
6. To join together _____
7. To make corrections or improvements _____
8. An opinion formed without judging fairly _____
9. Action done over and over for skill _____
10. To be a regular customer of something _____
11. To list by items _____
12. To make standard in size, weight, shape, etc. _____
13. A person who aids another in committing a crime _____
14. A change in appearance to look like someone else _____
15. To find fault with something _____

SKILL DRILL 3

Complete each of the following words by adding either *ise*, *ize*, or *ice* to form words from the Study List. Write the words you have formed on the lines provided.

1. item _ _ _ _____

2. accompli _ _ _ _____

3. improv _ _ _ _____

4. apprent _ _ _ _____

5. patron _ _ _ _____

6. critic _ _ _ _____

7. summar _ _ _ _____

8. standard _ _ _ _____

9. prejud _ _ _ _____

10. exerc _ _ _ _____

11. advert _ _ _ _____

12. disgu _ _ _ _____

13. pract _ _ _ _____

14. spl _ _ _ _____

15. rev _ _ _ _____

SKILL DRILL 4

Answer the following questions by using words from the Study List.

Which words end in *ice*?

1. _____

2. _____

3. _____

4. _____

5. _____

Which words end in *ise*?

6. _____

7. _____

8. _____

9. _____

10. _____

Which words end in *ize*?

11. _____

12. _____

13. _____

14. _____

15. _____

Study List

accomplice
advertise
apprentice
criticize
disguise
exercise
improvise
itemize
patronize
practice
prejudice
revise
splice
standardize
summarize

WORD GAME 12

The words from the Study List are used in this puzzle. The numbers of the clues match the numbers in the puzzle.

ACROSS

5. Make a list
7. Sell on TV
9. To find fault with something
10. Physical activity
12. Join together
13. To be a regular customer of something
14. A person who aids in a crime
15. An unfair opinion of something

DOWN

1. Person learning a trade
2. A change in appearance
3. To redo
4. To make standard in size or shape
6. To make a summary of something
8. Something done over and over for skill
11. To make up as you go along

HOW WELL CAN YOU SPELL?

Try to take this practice test without looking back at Lesson 12. After you have finished, check your work against the Study List. Correct any mistakes you have made.

A. One word in each of the following pairs of words is spelled incorrectly. Circle that word and spell it correctly on the line provided.

1. disguize, improvise   _____

2. accomplise, patronize   _____

3. itemize, splise   _____

4. prejudice, summarice   _____

5. criticice, standardize   _____

6. exercize, advertise   _____

7. revize, practice   _____

8. apprentise, splice   _____

B. In each of the following sentences, one word is spelled incorrectly. Find that word. Then spell it correctly on the line provided.

9. Our company will advertize the product on TV.   _____

10. Riding a bicycle takes plenty of practize.   _____

11. Please itemise all the supplies you will need.   _____

12. Ted was first to patronice our shop.   _____

13. Joanna will try to improvize her speech to the class.   _____

14. Try to vote without prejudise.   _____

15. Exact measurements will help to standardice our baked goods.   _____

Her Best Shot

When Maren Seidler was 13, her father told her, "See this iron ball? I think that with this you'll see all the countries of the world." With her father as her first coach, Maren managed to break the shot-put record for her age group. She has traveled the globe competing. Today she is the best female shot-putter in American history.

"Even if it's done well, not many spectators get much out of seeing it," says Maren. She refers to the fact that shot-putting does not attract many people—either as players or as watchers. Few people have knowledge of the sport. Even fewer realize that it is a sport for women as well as men.

Shot-putting is a simple contest of strength and balance. A shot-putter must throw an iron ball from inside a seven-foot circle. Like a dancer, the shot-putter must have complete body control. The athlete must put all her or his energy into throwing the iron ball, without leaving the circle. The iron ball is called a shot. A women's shot weighs 8 pounds 13 ounces. The men's is about twice as heavy. Maren holds the American Women's record for hurling this cannonball. She has thrown it a distance of 62 feet 7¾ inches. That's almost a quarter the length of a football field!

Music is Maren's inspiration. "I crave music," she says. She listens to classical music in the morning "to awaken with clarity." Before training, she listens to rock music "to really blast." And at night it's rhythm and blues. All that music must be doing the trick. Maren has won over 20 national shot-putting titles.

REVIEWING YOUR READING

Circle the letter beside the word or phrase that best completes the sentence.

1. Maren Seidler is the best female

   a. runner in the world.
   b. shot-putter in American history.
   c. runner in American history.
   d. shot-putter in the world.

2. Shot-putting is a sport for

   a. dancers.
   b. runners.
   c. women only.
   d. both men and women.

3. Shot-putters throw

   a. a bowling ball.
   b. a copper ball.
   c. an iron ball.
   d. a rubber ball.

4. Shot-putters must throw the ball from within a

   a. 3-foot circle.
   b. 5-foot square.
   c. 7-foot circle.
   d. 9-foot square.

5. The ball shot-putters use is called a

   a. shot.
   b. put.
   c. weight.
   d. bomb.

6. Maren Seidler's inspiration is

   a. television.
   b. books.
   c. music.
   d. movies.

7. Maren Seidler holds the women's

   a. American shot-put record.
   b. European shot-put record.
   c. American running record.
   d. Russian gymnastics record.

8. According to the story, you can conclude that Maren became interested in shot put through her

   a. gym teacher.
   b. father.
   c. mother.
   d. English teacher.

FIGURING THE FACTS

Decide whether the following statements are true or false. Write _T_ on the line if the statement is true. If the statement is false, cross out the incorrect word or phrase in the sentence. Then write the correct word or phrase on the line to make the statement true.

1. Maren has competed all over the globe.   _____

2. Maren's first coach was her brother.   _____

3. At the age of 13, Maren broke the world shot-put
    record for her age group.   _____

4. Shot-putting does not attract many people.   _____

5. Shot-putting is a simple test of quickness.   _____

6. The shot-putter must have complete body control.   _____

7. The women's shot weighs more than the men's.   _____

8. Maren has thrown the shot more than half the length
    of a football field.   _____

9. Maren listens to classical music just before training.   _____

10. Maren has won 150 national titles.   _____

WHAT'S YOUR OPINION?

1. The women's shot weighs less than the men's. Do you think they should be equal?
    Why or why not?

    _____

    _____

    _____

    _____

2. Why do you think that shot-putting is not a popular sport?

    _____

    _____

    _____

    _____

DEVELOPING SPELLING SKILLS

Study List

attract
compact
construct
distract
impact
inspector
knowledge
language
managed
mileage
privilege
salvage
spectators
vegetable
wreckage

The following words appear in the reading selection.

managed   knowledge   spectators   attract

Words like these pose special problems in spelling. For example, *managed* and *knowledge* have the same *j* sound but it is spelled differently in each. This *j* sound can be spelled *g*, *ge*, *dge*, and, of course, *j*. The most confusing are the words in which the sound is spelled *g* or *dge*, as in *managed* and *knowledge*.

Words like *spectators* and *attract* contain the letter combination *ct*. In spelling words with this consonant combination, it's easy to forget either the *c* or the *t*.

On your left is a Study List of words. Some are examples of the *j* sound spelled *ge* or *dge*, while others contain the *ct* consonant combination.

SKILL DRILL 1

Rewrite each of the following words on the lines provided. Then circle the *ge*, *dge*, or *ct* in each.

1. vegetable   _____

2. privilege   _____

3. inspector   _____

4. mileage   _____

5. language   _____

6. wreckage   _____

7. construct   _____

8. salvage   _____

9. spectators   _____

10. impact   _____

11. managed   _____

12. knowledge   _____

13. distract   _____

14. compact   _____

15. attract   _____

SKILL DRILL 2

The following are short definitions of words from the Study List. Fill the blanks with words from the Study List that match the definitions. If you need help, check the Mini-Dictionary in the back of this book.

1. Human speech, spoken or written   _____

2. Controlled or handled   _____

3. Miles covered or traveled   _____

4. The remains of something ruined   _____

5. A special right or advantage   _____

6. A person who checks or looks over carefully   _____

7. People who watch an event   _____

8. To rescue or save from being thrown away   _____

9. A plant used for food   _____

10. To draw something or someone to oneself   _____

11. What one knows   _____

12. Firmly packed together; small   _____

13. To put together or build   _____

14. Draw away, confuse, or disturb   _____

15. Collision; the striking of one thing against another   _____

SKILL DRILL 3

Fill in the blanks in each of the following words to form words from the Study List. Then write the words you have formed on the lines provided.

1. con _ _ ru _ _ _____

2. sp _ _ _ at _ _ s _____

3. v _ _ _ table _____

4. lan _ _ a _ _ _____

5. mile _ _ _ _____

6. in _ _ e _ _ or _____

7. di _ _ ra _ _ _____

8. comp _ _ _ _____

9. salv _ _ _ _____

10. attr _ _ _ _____

11. man _ _ _ d _____

12. pri _ _ le _ _ _____

13. kn _ _ le _ _ _ _____

14. _ _ eck _ _ _ _____

15. imp _ _ _ _____

SKILL DRILL 4

Answer the following questions by using words from the Study List.

Which words contain the word part *spect*?

1. _____   2. _____

Which word contains the word *table*?

3. _____

Which word contains the word *ledge*?

4. _____

Which word contains the word part *lege*?

5. _____

Which words contain the word *act*?

6. _____   7. _____

8. _____   9. _____

Study List

attract
compact
construct
distract
impact
inspector
knowledge
language
managed
mileage
privilege
salvage
spectators
vegetable
wreckage

Which word contains the word part *struct*?

10. _____

Which words contain the word *age*?

11. _____   **12.** _____

13. _____   **14.** _____

15. _____

▼

WORD GAME 13

The words from the Study List are scrambled on the left. Unscramble each word and write it correctly in the spaces on the right. If you unscramble the words correctly, you will find the answer to the puzzle question by reading the shaded column downward. Write your answer on the line below.

TRAATTC

APMOCCT

ROTATCEPSS

VSLAGEA

MIPCAT

REWKCGAE

EGAUGNAL

SNOCTURTC

SPINCEOTR

NOKLWDEGE

ANAGMED

GEEVATLBE

SIDARTCT

MEGAELI

RIPVELGEI

What did Maren Seidler's father tell her to do in order

to see the world? _____

HOW WELL CAN YOU SPELL?

Try to take this practice test without looking back at **Lesson 13**. After you have finished, check your work against the Study List. Correct any mistakes you have made.

A. One word in each of the following pairs of words is spelled incorrectly. Circle that word and spell it correctly on the line provided.

1. wreckadge, salvage   _____

2. language, miledge   _____

3. specktators, managed   _____

4. construct, priviledge   _____

5. distrat, compact   _____

6. inspektor, vegetable   _____

7. impakt, knowledge   _____

8. attract, salvadge   _____

B. In each of the following sentences, one word is spelled incorrectly. Find that word. Then spell it correctly on the line provided.

9. Compaked cars get much better mileage.   _____

10. Football attracks many spectators.   _____

11. It is always good to have a green vegitable with dinner.   _____

12. Next year the students will be studying a foreign languadge.   _____

13. The engineers will construkt a bridge across the river.   _____

14. The climbers manadged to descend the mountain unharmed.   _____

15. This job requires a knowlege of science and chemistry.   _____

14

André

"What a relief," said Harry Goodridge as he saw André swim into the harbor. André hopped out of the water and greeted his adopted father with a handshake and a slobbery kiss. The kiss was especially wet and slobbery, since André is a seal.

More than ten years ago, Goodridge found André at the entrance to Rockport Harbor in Maine. The playful pup was jumping in and out of fishing boats. Sometimes André would tip the boats over. This would always cause confusion. At first people were amused. But soon they got tired of losing their daily catch of fish to the hungry seal. It seems that when André would tip over a boat, he would also get a delicious dinner. Goodridge decided to take André in before the seal wound up in someone's net. So he built André a 32-foot pen overlooking the harbor.

The winters in Rockport, Maine, are very severe. For this reason, Goodridge made plans for André to spend the winter months at the New England Aquarium in Boston. Every spring the workers at the Aquarium drain André's tank and lead him to the Atlantic Ocean. André dives in and swims 160 miles to his home in Rockport's harbor. Goodridge is always relieved when he sees André enter the harbor. He fears that someday André will meet a female seal and forget about his harbor home.

Today André is the town hero of Rockport. The people have built a statue of André. Tourists come from miles just to see his whiskered face and handsome blue-gray fur coat. They also come to catch André's daily performance. At four o'clock every day, André does a series of stunts for the crowd to earn his daily allowance of fish. Following the show, Goodridge passes a bucket through the crowd for donations. After all, fish are expensive, especially when you're feeding a 220-pound seal!

REVIEWING YOUR READING

Circle the letter beside the word or phrase that best completes the sentence.

1. André is a
   a. boy.
   b. dolphin.
   c. seal.
   d. dog.

2. Harry Goodridge found André at the entrance to
   a. Boston Harbor.
   b. Rockport Harbor.
   c. Rockaway Harbor.
   d. New York Harbor.

3. When Goodridge found André he was
   a. jumping in and out of fishing boats.
   b. jumping in and out of house boats.
   c. performing tricks for tourists.
   d. working at the aquarium.

4. Goodridge built André a
   a. 23-foot pool.
   b. 23-foot pen.
   c. 32-foot pen.
   d. 32-foot boat.

5. The winters in Rockport, Maine, are
   a. very mild.
   b. very severe.
   c. sunny and warm.
   d. fair and warm.

6. André spends his winters at the
   a. Rockport Harbor.
   b. Rockport Aquarium.
   c. Miami Aquarium.
   d. New England Aquarium.

7. André's swimming trip from Boston to Maine is
   a. 64 miles.
   b. 160 miles.
   c. 1000 miles.
   d. 3000 miles.

8. According to the story, you can conclude that today the people of Rockport
   a. dislike André.
   b. like André.
   c. want André to leave town.
   d. wish André were a whale.

FIGURING THE FACTS

Decide whether the following statements are true or false. Write *T* on the line if the statement is true. If the statement is false, cross out the incorrect word or phrase in the sentence. Then write the correct word or phrase on the line to make the statement true.

1. Harry Goodridge is André's adopted father. _____
2. André was tipping over boats in order to eat. _____
3. André's pen overlooks the town library. _____
4. André dislikes the taste of fresh fish. _____
5. Each spring the aquarium workers lead André to the Pacific Ocean. _____
6. André swims 160 miles to Rockport's harbor. _____
7. The town of Rockport put up a painting of André. _____
8. André has a handsome blue-gray fur coat. _____
9. André earns his dinner by singing. _____
10. André weighs 220 pounds. _____

WHAT'S YOUR OPINION?

1. Do you think that André should be allowed to roam free? Why or why not?

_____
_____
_____
_____
_____

2. What would you do if you found an animal that was hungry and in danger of being killed?

_____
_____
_____
_____
_____
_____

DEVELOPING SPELLING SKILLS

Study List

acceptance
acquaintance
advance
allowance
appearance
assistance
clearance
distance
endurance
entrance
ignorance
importance
insurance
performance
remembrance

The following words appear in the reading selection.

allowance   distance   entrance   performance

All of these words end with the suffix *ance*. These words are often confused with words that end in *ence*. There is no rule governing these endings. Therefore, these words must be memorized.

On your left is a Study List of words. All end with the suffix *ance*. The words may look difficult because they are long. However, many are simply longer forms of words you have already studied. For example, *allowance* is *allow* plus the suffix *ance*. You will find that these words will be easy to spell once you begin to work with them. In the next chapter we will work with words that end in *ence*. If you know these words you will have little trouble learning those in the next chapter.

SKILL DRILL 1

Rewrite each of the following words on the lines provided. Then circle the *ance* **ending in each.**

1. insurance _____
2. acquaintance _____
3. ignorance _____
4. performance _____
5. advance _____
6. appearance _____
7. clearance _____

8. acceptance _____
9. entrance _____
10. importance _____
11. remembrance _____
12. allowance _____
13. assistance _____
14. distance _____

15. endurance _____

SKILL DRILL 2

The following are short definitions of words from the Study List. Fill the blanks with words from the Study List that match the definitions. If you need help, check the Mini-Dictionary in the back of this book.

1. The quality of being important _____
2. Insuring of life, person, or property _____
3. The acting of a show, movie, etc. _____
4. The act of remembering _____
5. To move forward _____
6. Help or aid _____
7. The act of clearing a space _____
8. Power to keep on or last _____
9. The act of taking something offered or given _____
10. The space between two things, places, or people _____
11. A person you know but not as a close friend _____
12. The place through which to enter _____
13. A lack of knowledge _____
14. A limited share of money or goods that is allowed to be given _____
15. The act of coming into sight or appearing _____

SKILL DRILL 3

Fill the blanks in each of the following words to form a word from the Study List. Then write the word you have formed on the line provided.

1. a _ _ ear _ nce _____

2. en _ r _ nce _____

3. en _ ur _ nce _____

4. a _ _ i _ t _ nce _____

5. a _ _ _ a _ nt _ nce _____

6. dis _ _ nce _____

7. r _ _ _ _ br _ nce _____

8. im _ _ _ t _ nce _____

9. in _ _ _ _ nce _____

10. per _ _ _ mance _____

11. a _ _ ow _ nce _____

12. a _ _ e _ _ _ nce _____

13. ad _ _ nce _____

14. cl _ _ r _ nce _____

15. ig _ _ r _ nce _____

SKILL DRILL 4

Answer the following questions by using words from the Study List.

Which words begin with the prefix *en*?

1. _____   2. _____

Which word begins with the prefix *in*?

3. _____

Which word begins with the prefix *dis*?

4. _____

Which word begins with the prefix *re*?

5. _____

Which word begins with the prefix *ad*?

6. _____

Which word begins with the prefix *ignor*?

7. _____

Which word begins with the prefix *appear*?

8. _____

Which word contains the word *assist*?

9. _____

Which word contains the word *import*?

10. _____

Which word contains the word *perform*?

11. _____

Which word contains the word *acquaint*?

12. _____

Which word contains the word *allow*?

13. _____

Which word contains the word *accept*?

14. _____

Which word contains the word *clear*?

15. _____

Study List

acceptance
acquaintance
advance
allowance
appearance
assistance
clearance
distance
endurance
entrance
ignorance
importance
insurance
performance
remembrance

WORD GAME 14

This is a puzzle without clues! Study the length and spelling of each Study List word. Then figure out which words from the Study List fit into the spaces. Once you have found the first word, the others will be easy to find. Some of the letters have been given to you.

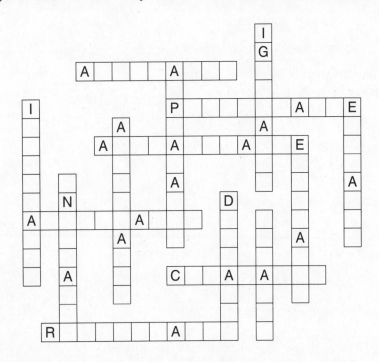

HOW WELL CAN YOU SPELL?

Try to take this practice test without looking back at Lesson 14. After you have finished, check your work against the Study List. Correct any mistakes you have made.

A. One word in each of the following pairs of words is spelled incorrectly. Circle that word and spell it correctly on the line provided.

1. ignorence, insurance   _____

2. acceptance, remembrence   _____

3. clearence, entrance   _____

4. allowence, endurance   _____

5. distance, acquaintence   _____

6. performance, advance   _____

7. importance, assistence   _____

8. appearence, ignorance   _____

B. In each of the following sentences, one word is spelled incorrectly. Find that word. Then spell it correctly on the line provided.

9. The distence between the two cities is 50 miles.   _____

10. Joanne received her letter of acceptence today.   _____

11. You should have an insurence policy for your car.   _____

12. Please wait for me by the entrence.   _____

13. James will advence in his company.   _____

14. Hiking is a test of strength and endurence.   _____

15. Ed isn't aware of the importence of knowing mathematics.   _____

Our Trace

"I can't bear being called a wacky, zany comedienne," says Tracey Ullman. "I'm not a comedienne. I'm a character actress. I couldn't get up to tell a joke to save my life."

Tracey grew up in a suburb of London. She calls it "the kind of place where you are a success if you simply make it out of the neighborhood." Her father died when she was six years old. That left her mother to care for Tracey and her older sister. "My mum worked in a laboratory testing food," Tracey explains. "She'd often bring home samples for our dinner. Sometimes she'd have to report that product X had been unfit for humans!"

Tracey's mother was a big influence on her career, encouraging Tracey to sing and tell jokes. She would also perform plays with her. Tracey's talent for mimicking different voices came from imitating neighborhood kids. She did it in order to fit in. "I had to talk like them to avoid being beaten up!" Tracey says.

At age 12, Tracey won a scholarship to an acting school. She claims that she didn't learn very much there. But it did help her to develop a sense of confidence. She also began to set goals for herself. Eventually, Tracey got a part in *The Rocky Horror Picture Show*. She went on to record four hit records. She also performed on several British TV shows. Tracey became so popular that the English viewing audience began to call her "Our Trace."

But no one in America knew who she was. An appearance on *Late Night with David Letterman* changed things. Her quick humor helped her to get a show of her own. On her show she sings, dances, and portrays a variety of characters. "I get to do everything I want in this show," Tracey explains. "This is a golden time for me."

REVIEWING YOUR READING

Circle the letter beside the word or phrase that best completes the sentence.

1. Tracey Ullman calls herself

   a. a zany comedienne.
   b. a character actress.
   c. a stand-up comic.
   d. a comic personality.

2. When Tracey was six years old,

   a. her mother died.
   b. she won a scholarship.
   c. her father died.
   d. she performed her first play.

3. Tracey's mother worked in

   a. a laboratory testing machines.
   b. a hospital.
   c. show business.
   d. a laboratory testing food.

4. Tracey won a scholarship to acting school when she was

   a. 12 years old.
   b. 6 years old.
   c. 21 years old.
   d. 18 years old.

5. You can conclude that as a child Tracey

   a. was well liked by the other kids.
   b. had a hard time "fitting in" with neighborhood kids.
   c. was quiet and shy.
   d. was a professional actress.

6. Tracey claims that in acting school,

   a. she learned quite a lot.
   b. she learned how to sing.
   c. she didn't learn much.
   d. she studied dancing.

7. Tracey developed her talent for mimicking voices by

   a. listening to records.
   b. imitating her teachers.
   c. watching television.
   d. imitating neighborhood kids.

8. You can conclude that before coming to America, Tracey was

   a. a big star in England.
   b. unknown in her own country.
   c. already an international star.
   d. quite popular in Canada.

FIGURING THE FACTS

Decide whether the following statements are true or false. Write *T* on the line if the statement is true. If the statement is false, cross out the incorrect word or phrase in the sentence. Then write the correct word or phrase on the line to make the statement true.

1. Tracey Ullman doesn't like being called an actress.   _____

2. She grew up in a suburb of London.   _____

3. Tracey's mother often brought home samples of new foods for dinner.   _____

4. Tracey received a scholarship to college.   _____

5. Tracey Ullman has one older sister.   _____

6. *The Rocky Horror Picture Show* is a film that Tracey appeared in.   _____

7. In England Tracey made 40 hit records.   _____

8. The British people call her "Our Little Tracey."   _____

9. Tracey once appeared on *Late Night with David Letterman.*   _____

10. On Tracey's TV show, she sings, dances, and acts.   _____

WHAT'S YOUR OPINION?

1. Tracey Ullman's confidence in her talent has brought her a long way. Why do you think it is important to have confidence in yourself?

_____

_____

_____

_____

_____

2. Tracey learned how to set goals for herself. Do you think it is helpful to set goals for yourself? Why or why not?

_____

_____

_____

_____

_____

_____

DEVELOPING SPELLING SKILLS

Study List

absence
audience
circumference
coincidence
commence
confidence
convenience
correspondence
difference
existence
experience
independence
influence
reference

The following words appear in the reading selection.

audience   confidence   influence

All of these words end with the suffix *ence*. Words that end with this suffix are often confused with words that end in *ance*. As you saw in Lesson 14, there is no rule to tell us when to use *ence* and when to use *ance*. Therefore, these words must be memorized.

On your left is a Study List of words. All the words end in *ence*. These words may look difficult because they are long, but actually most of them are quite easy to spell.

SKILL DRILL 1

Rewrite each of the following words on the lines provided. Then circle the *ence* **ending in each.**

1. correspondence _____

2. experience _____

3. commence _____

4. reference _____

5. absence _____

6. existence _____

7. difference _____

8. influence _____

9. confidence _____

10. convenience _____

11. independence _____

12. audience _____

13. circumference _____

14. coincidence _____

SKILL DRILL 2

The following are short definitions of words from the Study List. Fill in the blanks with words from the Study List that match the definitions. If you need help, check the Mini-Dictionary in the back of this book.

1. Freedom from control or help of another _____

2. Quality of being convenient or handy _____

3. A chance meeting that is remarkable _____

4. A firm belief in oneself _____

5. Everything you have ever felt or done, or what has happened to you _____

6. The condition of being different; unlikeness _____

7. An exchange of letters, or letter writing _____

8. To start or begin _____

9. People gathered in a place to hear or see something _____

10. The boundary line of a circle _____

11. Life; the state of being _____

12. To have power over another _____

13. The state of being away _____

14. The act of referring or consulting _____

SKILL DRILL 3

Fill the blanks in each of the following words to form words from the Study List. Then write the word you have formed on the line provided.

1. a _ _ _ nce _____

2. in _ _ u _ nce _____

3. cir _ _ m _ _ r _ nce _____

4. co _ _ en _ _ _ _____

5. co _ fi _ _ nce _____

6. di _ _ er _ nce _____

7. con _ _ n _ _ nce _____

8. in _ _ pen _ _ nce _____

9. c _ _ nci _ _ nce _____

10. e _ _ er _ _ nce _____

11. c _ rr _ _ pon _ _ nce _____

12. a _ d _ _ nce _____

13. e _ is _ _ nce _____

14. r _ _ e _ _ nce _____

SKILL DRILL 4

Answer the following questions by using words from the Study List.

Which words begin wtih the prefix *con*?

1. _____   2. _____

Which words begin with the prefix *in*.

3. _____   4. _____

Which word begins with the prefix *circum*?

5. _____

Which word begins with the prefix *ab*?

6. _____

Which word contains the word *refer*?

7. _____

Which word contains the word *differ*?

8. _____

Which word contains the word *correspond*?

9. _____

Study List

absence
audience
circumference
coincidence
commence
confidence
convenience
correspondence
difference
existence
experience
independence
influence
reference

Which word contains the word *coincide*?

10. _____

Which words begin with the prefix *ex*?

11. _____   **12.** _____

Which word begins with the prefix *com*?

13. _____

Which word begins with the prefix *audi*?

14. _____

WORD GAME 15

This is a puzzle without any clues! Study the length and spelling of each Study List word. Then figure out which words from the Study List fit in the spaces. Once you have found the first word, the rest will be easy to find. Some of the letters have been given to you.

HOW WELL CAN YOU SPELL?

Try to take this practice test without looking back at Lesson 15. After you have finished, check your work against the Study List. Correct any mistakes you have made.

A. One word in each of the following pairs of words is spelled incorrectly. Circle that word and spell it correctly on the line provided.

1. existance, difference   _____

2. conveniance, influence   _____

3. independence, audiance   _____

4. referance, experience   _____

5. coincidance, confidence   _____

6. circumferance, absence   _____

7. correspondance, reference   _____

8. commance, audience   _____

B. In each of the following sentences, one word is spelled incorrectly. Find that word. Then spell it correctly on the line provided.

9. Don is working at the restaurant to get experiance cooking.   _____

10. You will have to make up that absance from class.   _____

11. The audiance stood as the president entered the room.   _____

12. Mary has all the self-confidance she needs.   _____

13. In 1776, America declared its independance from Britain.   _____

14. Television has a great influance on our culture.   _____

15. The differance between the two countries is very small.   _____

Tuned In

Although you may not have heard of him, Nam June Paik can be called the father of music video. He was the first artist to make use of television. One of his works, called *TV Moon*, has a dozen TVs showing the rise and fall of the moon. By tinkering with electronics, Paik changes the images on TV screens. The screen is his canvas. But you'll find no country scene or bowl of fruit in this painting. Nam June certainly has a taste for the unusual.

Nam June was born in Korea, but moved to Japan when he was very young. As a child, he was fascinated by the radio. He would listen for hours and hours. Often he would ask, "Why do people hide in the box?"

With the invention of television, his interest widened. Nam June was spellbound by the magic images that appeared on the screen. Determined to study electronics, he made his way to Germany. By that time, he had already studied art and music. On the piano, he could perform everything from popular to classical music. In Germany, Nam June put his knowledge of music and electronics together. The result was electronic music. His compositions became so popular that even the Beatles became fans.

But Nam June didn't stop with success. A person who studied radar told him that radar waves made interesting patterns. "Then I had an idea," Nam June says. "Why don't I move from electronic music to electronic painting with the TV?" And he did.

In the early 1960s he had his first show of "electronic paintings." It was the world's first video art show. There were 13 TV sets with scrambled images. Paik had learned enough about televisions to be able to control the pictures the way he wanted.

Now, after 20 years of tinkering with TV sets, he is a great success. His TV art has been seen in museums around the world. He has even had a show at the famous Whitney Museum of American Art in New York. You could say that people are finally getting "turned on" by his art!

REVIEWING YOUR READING

Circle the letter beside the word or phrase that best completes the sentence.

1. Nam June Paik can be called the

   a. father of rock music.
   b. artist of the century.
   c. father of music video.
   d. father of television.

2. Paik was the first artist to make use of

   a. radio.
   b. electricity.
   c. laser beams.
   d. television.

3. Nam June Paik was born in

   a. Korea.
   b. the United States.
   c. Japan.
   d. Germany.

4. As a child Nam June was fascinated by

   a. movies.
   b. computers.
   c. rock music.
   d. radio.

5. As a boy Nam June studied how to play the

   a. cello.
   b. piano.
   c. electric guitar.
   d. violin.

6. One of Paik's works is called

   a. *13 Moons.*
   b. *TV Moon.*
   c. *The Rise of the Moon.*
   d. *Radio Wave Moon.*

7. Nam June invented electronic painting by studying

   a. television repair.
   b. radios.
   c. radar waves.
   d. the music of the Beatles.

8. You can come to the conclusion that Nam June Paik

   a. likes to try new ideas.
   b. does not try new ideas.
   c. is not very successful.
   d. is no longer creating artworks.

FIRST THINGS FIRST

Some of the events in Nam June Paik's life are listed below. Reread the story, paying close attention to the order in which things happened. Then write the numbers from 1 to 8 beside the sentences in the order in which things happened.

_____   He moved to Japan at a young age.

_____   The invention of TV caused him to widen his interests.

_____   Nam June composed electronic music.

_____   Paik learned about radar waves.

_____   As a boy in Japan he found the radio fascinating.

_____   He moved to Germany to study electronics.

_____   He began to use televisions to make "electronic paintings."

_____   Nam June Paik was born in Korea.

WHAT'S YOUR OPINION?

1. Nam June Paik's art was different from anyone else's. It was original—no one had ever done anything like it. Why is it important to be original?

_____

_____

_____

_____

_____

2. Nam June could have stopped being an artist with his first success in electronic music but he didn't. Why do you think he kept creating new things? Is it important to keep working? Why?

_____

_____

_____

_____

_____

DEVELOPING SPELLING SKILLS

Study List

ceiling
sealing
council
counsel
flair
flare
morning
mourning
rap
wrap
ring
wring
scene
seen
complement
compliment

The following words appear in the reading selection.

scene   seen

These words sound alike, but they are spelled differently. They also mean different things.

Scene means a time or place   *Seen* means having looked at

These words are homophones. A **homophone** is a word that has the same sound as another word, but a different spelling and meaning.

To the left is a Study List of words. Each word is a homophone. Homophones are very easily confused. It is important to remember the spelling as well as the meaning of each. Some of these you may already know.

Definitions of Study List Words:

ceiling   the inside top covering of a room
sealing   closing tightly

council   a group of people called together to talk things over
counsel   to advise

flair   a natural talent
flare   a dazzling burst of flame or light

morning   the early part of the day
mourning   showing sorrow for someone's death

rap   to strike sharply
wrap   to cover with paper and string

ring   to make a clear sound by touching or striking
wring   to squeeze or twist

scene   the time or place of a play or story
seen   having looked at

complement   to make something complete
compliment   something said in praise of someone

SKILL DRILL 1

Rewrite each of the following words on the lines provided.

1. morning _____
2. ceiling _____
3. council _____
4. mourning _____
5. compliment _____
6. counsel _____
7. ring _____
8. rap _____

9. scene _____
10. sealing _____
11. flair _____
12. seen _____
13. flare _____
14. complement _____
15. wrap _____
16. wring _____

SKILL DRILL 2

The following are short definitions of words from the Study List. Fill the blanks with words from the Study List that match the definitions. If you need help, check the Mini-Dictionary in the back of this book.

1. The time or place of a play or story _____
2. A natural talent _____
3. A group of people called together to talk things over _____
4. Closing tightly _____
5. A dazzling burst of flame or light _____
6. Something said in praise _____
7. Having looked at _____
8. Showing sorrow for someone's death _____
9. The inside top covering of a room _____
10. To squeeze or twist _____
11. To cover with paper and string _____
12. To strike sharply _____
13. To make a clear sound by touching or striking _____
14. To make something complete _____
15. To advise _____
16. The early part of the day _____

SKILL DRILL 3

Answer the following questions by using words from the Study List.

Which words end with the letters *ment*?

1. _____   2. _____

Which word contains the word *air*?

3. _____

Which word contains the word *are*?

4. _____

Which words end with the letter *p*?

5. _____   6. _____

Which word contains the vowel combination *ee*?

7. _____

Which word ends with the letters *ne*?

8. _____

Which words begin with the letters *coun*?

9. _____   10. _____

Which words end with the letters *ing*?

11. _____   12. _____

13. _____   14. _____

15. _____   16. _____

Study List
ceiling
sealing
council
counsel
flair
flare
morning
mourning
rap
wrap
ring
wring
scene
seen
complement
compliment

SKILL DRILL 4

Fill the blanks in the following sentences by choosing the correct homophone in parentheses. Write it on the line provided.

1. Our family is (morning, mourning) _____ the death of Uncle Ralph.

2. Mr. Sweeney will (council, counsel) _____ the class on career choices.

3. Mrs. Adams will be (sealing, ceiling) _____ the jars with wax.

4. The light is hanging from the (sealing, ceiling) _____.

5. The (seen, scene) _____ of the novel is New York City.

6. Kurt has a (flare, flair) _____ for performing.

7. He paid me a (compliment, complement) _____ on my shirt.

8. The light from the (flare, flair) _____ brightened the sky.

9. I have (seen, scene) _____ many hats like that one.

10. The blueberries are the perfect (compliment, complement) _____ to the fruit salad.

11. (Ring, Wring) _____ the bell again to see if they are home.

12. There will be a meeting of the student (council, counsel) _____.

13. The postmaster asks that we (rap, wrap) _____ our packages carefully.

14. Did someone (wrap, rap) _____ on the window a few minutes ago?

15. If you (wring, ring) _____ the shirt out, it will dry quickly.

16. We have a good breakfast every (morning, mourning) _____.

WORD GAME 16

The words from the Study List are used in this puzzle. The numbers of the clues match the numbers of the puzzle. Read the clues below. Then write your answers in the puzzle blocks.

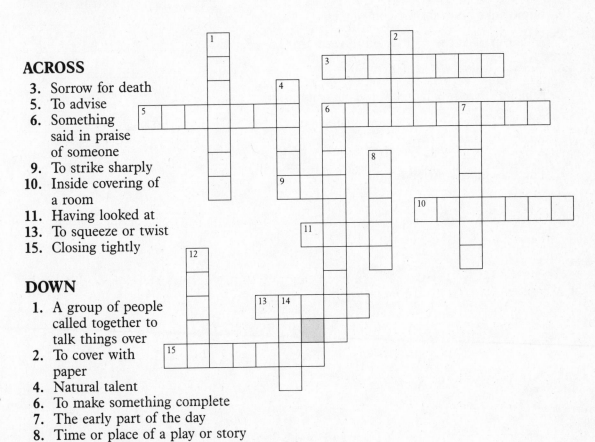

ACROSS

3. Sorrow for death
5. To advise
6. Something said in praise of someone
9. To strike sharply
10. Inside covering of a room
11. Having looked at
13. To squeeze or twist
15. Closing tightly

DOWN

1. A group of people called together to talk things over
2. To cover with paper
4. Natural talent
6. To make something complete
7. The early part of the day
8. Time or place of a play or story
12. A burst of light
14. To make a sound by touching or striking a bell

HOW WELL CAN YOU SPELL?

Try to take this practice test without looking back at Lesson 16. After you have finished, check your work against the Study List. Correct any mistakes you have made.

One word in each of the following sentences is spelled incorrectly. Find that word. Then spell it correctly on the line provided.

1. This salad will compliment the picnic lunch.   _____

2. Susan has shown a flare for drawing.   _____

3. The sealing in the kitchen is quite high.   _____

4. The city counsel is meeting this afternoon.   _____

5. The coach will be the one to council you on athletics.   _____

6. Many students have already scene the exhibit.   _____

7. Ellen is morning the death of her pet cat.   _____

8. The secretaries will be ceiling the envelopes with tape.   _____

9. The bus will leave early tomorrow mourning.   _____

10. She thanked him for the complement.   _____

11. A flair marked the spot where the accident happened.   _____

12. Did you hear the telephone wring?   _____

13. Ring out the towel before you hang it up to dry.   _____

14. Don't rap the gift until I get home.   _____

15. The seen of the play was Boston in the 1930s.   _____

16. The baby likes to wrap on the table.   _____

Magnificent Marathon

Friends, reporters, and television crews gathered to wish Patty Wilson good luck. Her goal was to run from Buena Park, California, to Portland, Oregon. The distance is 1,000 miles. As the music rose from the local band, Patty broke the paper banner that marked her start.

This was an historic marathon because Patty has epilepsy. That means she suffers from a disorder that brings about seizures. Seizures are spells that cause people to shake and to black out.

On her run, Patty carried the Candle of Understanding. It is the symbol of the Epilepsy Foundation of America. She hoped to show the world that the word "handicapped" doesn't mean "unable."

During the first 25 miles, Patty fractured a bone in her foot. A doctor advised her not to continue. But Patty was determined. She kept running, averaging 31 miles a day. Patty's father kept her company on the trip. At night they slept in a small van, and each morning they rose at 4:30 to prepare for running. By 6:00 A.M. they were on the road. Patty fought steep hills and stiff winds. She ignored the painful blisters on her feet. Along the way, people came out to greet her. Many were handicapped. They cheered her on and, sometimes, even ran along with her.

After six weeks, the ordeal was over. She had finally reached Portland. Crowds of well-wishers lined the streets. People cheered and waved. Some even cried. Patty could hardly smile because of the pain in her feet. But she was overjoyed. She had not only proved her point, but also set a world record for distance. The governor of Oregon proclaimed July 28 as Patty Wilson Day. It was a special day for anyone who has ever been called "handicapped." "I haven't stopped running because of my epilepsy," says Patty. "I never will."

REVIEWING YOUR READING

Circle the letter beside the word or phrase that best completes the sentence.

1. Patty Wilson ran a total of

   a. 10 miles.
   b. 100 miles.
   c. 500 miles.
   d. 1,000 miles.

2. Patty ran from Buena Park, California, to

   a. Portland, Oregon.
   b. San Francisco, California.
   c. Wilson, Oregon.
   d. San Diego, California.

3. Patty suffers from

   a. broken bones.
   b. seizures.
   c. headaches.
   d. sores.

4. The symbol of the Epilepsy Foundation is the

   a. Flame of Light.
   b. Candle of Understanding.
   c. Light of Hope.
   d. Torch of Happiness.

5. During Patty's first 25 miles, she

   a. fractured a bone in her foot.
   b. quit running.
   c. broke her arm.
   d. suffered a seizure.

6. Patty averaged

   a. 31 miles per day.
   b. 60 miles per day.
   c. 100 miles per day.
   d. 1,000 miles per day.

7. Patty's marathon took a total of

   a. 2 weeks.
   b. 6 weeks.
   c. 16 weeks.
   d. 36 weeks.

8. According to the story, you can conclude that Patty Wilson will

   a. never run again.
   b. continue to run.
   c. become a professional runner.
   d. become a running coach.

FIGURING THE FACTS

Decide whether the following statements are true or false. Write _T_ on the line if the statement is true. If the statement is false, cross out the incorrect word or phrase in the sentence. Then write the correct word or phrase on the line to make the statement true.

1. Reporters came to see Patty begin her race.   _____

2. At the start of the marathon, there was a band playing.   _____

3. On her run, Patty carried the American flag.   _____

4. When Patty fractured a bone in her foot, the doctor told her to go on.   _____

5. Patty rose at 4:30 A.M. each day.   _____

6. Patty began her running at 12 noon each day.   _____

7. Patty made the trip all by herself.   _____

8. At the end of the marathon, there were blisters on Patty's feet.   _____

9. Patty Wilson set a world record for distance.   _____

10. In Oregon, July 28 is Patty Wilson Day.   _____

WHAT'S YOUR OPINION?

1. Why do you think Patty wanted to run her marathon?

_____

_____

_____

_____

_____

2. Patty proved that she could do an "impossible" feat. Do you believe that people can do the "impossible"? Why or why not?

_____

_____

_____

_____

_____

DEVELOPING SPELLING SKILLS

Study List

Arkansas
Atlantic Ocean
California
February
Fourth of July
governor of Oregon
June
Labor Day
mayor of Chicago
New Hampshire
Niagara Falls
September
Tuesday
United Nations
Wednesday

Capital letters tell us that something important is ahead. The first letter of every sentence *always* begins with a capital. And capitals are *always* used when spelling someone's name. However, capitalizing can become confusing when names contain more than one word. Sometimes we aren't sure whether a word is the name of something or not. Below are some rules to use as guidelines when you are in doubt about when to use capitals.

Rule: **Always capitalize the first word in a sentence.**

Example: Crowds of well-wishers lined the streets.

Rule: **Always capitalize days of the week, months, and holidays.**

Examples: Tuesday
June 18, 1977
Fourth of July

Notice that minor words like *of* are not capitalized.

Rule: **Always capitalize the names of people, titles (when used with the person's name), schools, and organizations.**

Examples: Patty Wilson
Governor Smith
United Nations

Rule: **Always capitalize the names of geographical terms or places like cities, states, countries, rivers, oceans, etc.**

Examples: California   Atlantic Ocean

There are more rules for capitals, which we will cover in Lesson 18.

Above is a Study List of words. All of these words apply to the rules of capitalization. If a word is supposed to be capitalized and is not, it is considered to be misspelled. Therefore, it is doubly important to know the spelling of these words, *and* to capitalize them.

SKILL DRILL 1

Rewrite each of the following words on the lines provided. Then circle the capit letters in each.

1. Tuesday _____
2. Wednesday _____
3. Atlantic Ocean _____
4. September _____
5. New Hampshire _____
6. Fourth of July _____
7. June _____

8. United Nations _____
9. Arkansas _____
10. California _____
11. mayor of Chicago _____
12. February _____
13. governor of Oregon _____
14. Niagara Falls _____

15. Labor Day _____

SKILL DRILL 2

Answer the following questions by using words from the Study List.

Which words are the names of states?

1. _____   2. _____
3. _____

Which words are the days of the week?

4. _____   5. _____

Which words are months of the year?

6. _____   7. _____
8. _____

Which is the name of an organization?

9. _____

Which are people's titles?

10. _____

Which words are the names of holidays?

12. _____   13. _____

Which words are the names of geographical areas?

14. _____   15. _____

SKILL DRILL 3

In the following sentences, certain Study List words should be capitalized. Find those words. Then rewrite them, correctly capitalized, on the lines provided.

1. The new class will begin next september.   _____

2. february is the second month of the year.   _____

3. The whole family will be taking the trip to niagara falls.   _____

4. New York borders on the atlantic ocean.   _____

5. The party will be held on labor day.   _____

6. Our nation's birthday is the fourth of july.   _____

7. The mayor of chicago will speak at today's luncheon.   _____

8. Canada is a member of the united nations.   _____

9. Patty began her marathon on june 18, 1977.   _____

10. Jean shook the hand of the governor of oregon.   _____

11. This week's meeting will be held on tuesday.   _____

12. On our way west, we will travel through arkansas.   _____

13. wednesday evening will be your last chance to see the film.   _____

14. new hampshire will be the first state to hold the election.   _____

15. Marge lives in Los Angeles, california.   _____

SKILL DRILL 4

Fill in the blanks in each of the following words to form words from the Study List. Then write the words you have formed on the lines provided. Be sure to capitalize where necessary.

1. se _ _ _ mber _____

2. united n _ _ ions _____

3. j _ ne _____

4. t _ _ sday _____

5. _ rk _ _ s _ s _____

6. wed _ _ _ day _____

7. gov _ _ n _ _ of oregon _____

8. _ eb _ _ ary _____

9. n _ _ gara falls _____

10. at _ _ _ tic
    oc _ _ n _____

11. l _ b _ r day _____

12. f _ _ rth of
    july _____

13. may _ _
    of Chicago _____

14. cal _ _ _ rn _ _ _____

15. new
    hamp _ _ ire _____

▼

WORD GAME 17

The words from the Study List are used in this puzzle. The numbers of the clues match the numbers of the puzzle. Read the clues below. Then write your answers in the puzzle blocks.

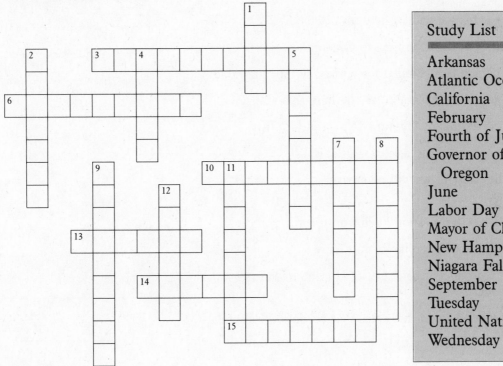

Study List

Arkansas
Atlantic Ocean
California
February
Fourth of July
Governor of
    Oregon
June
Labor Day
Mayor of Chicago
New Hampshire
Niagara Falls
September
Tuesday
United Nations
Wednesday

ACROSS

3. State that begins with capital *C*
6. Ninth month
9. New _____
13. _____ Nations
14. _____ of July
15. Mayor of _____

DOWN

1. Sixth month
2 Third day of the week
4. _____ Day
5. State that begins with a capital *A*
7. _____ Falls
8. Second month
9. Fourth day of the week
11. _____ Ocean
12. State that begins with a capital *O*

HOW WELL CAN YOU SPELL?

Try to take this practice test without looking back at Lesson 17. After you have finished, check your work against the Study List. Correct any mistakes you have made.

In each of the following sentences, one word is spelled incorrectly. Find that word. Then spell it correctly on the line provided. Remember that a word is misspelled if it is not capitalized when it should be.

1. For information you must write to the new hamshire Tourist Department.

   _____

2. The trip is set for the end of septimber.

   _____

3. The untied nations meets in New York City.

   _____

4. juen is the month that marks the beginning of summer.

   _____

5. The final exam will be held on tuseday.

   _____

6. arkansaw is the state next to Oklahoma.

   _____

7. The parade is scheduled for wednsday morning.

   _____

8. The governer of Oregon will be here this afternoon.

   _____

9. Jody's birthday is feburary 15.

   _____

10. The boat sailed close to niagra Falls.

    _____

11. On this voyage, we will be crossing the Atalantic Ocean.

    _____

12. This year, the vacation begins on laber Day.

    _____

13. The rent is due on the forth of July.

    _____

14. Carol introduced the mayer of chicago to the audience.

    _____

15. california is one of the states that borders the Pacific Ocean.

    _____

18

Jaws and Claws

Who could love a crocodile? They're surely not cuddly. And they aren't known for their friendly smiles. Yet the ancient Egyptians used to put gold bracelets on the legs of their toothy friends. Legend has it that they even built a city in their honor.

Today, crocodiles are more likely to end up as handbags or wallets. For this reason, "crocs" are quickly disappearing from the earth. Certain species are already extinct.

There are 21 different kinds of crocodiles. The American alligator is one of the few that is out of danger. Thanks to strict laws, the swamps of Louisiana and Florida are thick with "gators." There are so many that the government has had to hire special hunters to protect people from "troublemakers." Those are "gators" that find their way into cities and towns and threaten people's safety.

The students at the University of Florida have adopted their neighborhood gators as pets. They give names to the leathery lizards. They even pat them and feed them cookies! Experts claim that this kind of action is dangerous. The gators easily lose their natural fear of humans. Gators will attack if they feel threatened. They might even strike when looking for a tasty meal.

Although we think of crocs as violent animals, they are very good parents. When a mother croc lays her 40 to 80 eggs, the father stands guard. Mom covers the eggs with dirt and they both wait for about three months. When "peeping" sounds come from the ground, the eggs are hatching. The mother uncovers the eggs and takes the youngsters into her jaws. She carries them to their new home in a nearby pond. Both parents carefully watch the babies until they're old enough to defend themselves.

All this family talk brings us back to the question, who could love a crocodile? Why, another crocodile, of course!

REVIEWING YOUR READING

Circle the letter beside the word or phrase that best completes the sentence.

1. Ancient Egyptians decorated crocodiles with
   a. gold hats.
   b. gold bracelets.
   c. gloves.
   d. handbags.

2. The word *extinct* means
   a. disappeared from the earth.
   b. out of style.
   c. growing.
   d. increasing in number.

3. Certain species of crocodiles are disappearing from the earth because they are being used for
   a. hats and gloves.
   b. food and clothing.
   c. handbags and wallets.
   d. jewelry and perfume.

4. The American alligator is out of danger because it is protected by
   a. hunters.
   b. students.
   c. strict laws.
   d. troublesome gators.

5. Another title for this selection could be
   a. Handbags and Wallets.
   b. Troublemakers.
   c. Florida's Pets.
   d. Gators and Crocs.

6. Feeding gators can be dangerous because they
   a. eat too much.
   b. lose their fear of humans.
   c. eat too little.
   d. lose their fear of food.

7. According to the story, you can conclude that crocodiles are
   a. good parents.
   b. poor parents.
   c. good pets.
   d. poor swimmers.

8. A mother crocodile lays
   a. 40 to 80 eggs.
   b. 80 to 100 eggs.
   c. 100 to 150 eggs.
   d. 150 to 200 eggs.

FIGURING THE FACTS

Decide whether the following statements are true or false. Write *T* on the line if the statement is true. If the statement is false, cross out the incorrect word or phrase in the sentence. Then write the correct word or phrase on the line to make the statement true.

1. Legend has it that ancient Egyptians built a city in honor of the crocodile.   _____

2. Crocodiles are never dangerous to humans.   _____

3. There are 21 different kinds of crocodiles.   _____

4. The cities in Louisiana and Florida are thick with gators.   _____

5. "Troublemakers" are the gators who get into cities and towns.   _____

6. Students in Florida feed cookies to gators.   _____

7. Gators do not have a natural fear of humans.   _____

8. If a gator feels threatened, it will attack.   _____

9. Gator eggs are hatching when "peeping" sounds come from the ground.   _____

10. The eggs are usually uncovered by the father.   _____

WHAT'S YOUR OPINION?

1. Do you think it is right to use animal skins for handbags, wallets, and clothing? Why or why not?

_____

_____

_____

_____

_____

2. Do you think it is important to protect wild animals like crocodiles? Why or why not?

_____

_____

_____

_____

_____

DEVELOPING SPELLING SKILLS

Study List

August
Catcher in the Rye
Chinese
Egyptians
Germany
Louisiana
Mississippi River
New Year's Day
Rocky Mountains
Spanish
Sports Illustrated
Thanksgiving
The Scarlet Letter
Thursday
University of Florida

We use capital letters to begin a sentence and when spelling the names of persons, places, or things. Here is a list of rules to use as a guideline when in doubt about using capitals. Rules 1 and 2 are new and should be studied carefully. Rules 3 through 6 are a review of rules you have learned in previous lessons.

Rule 1: **Always capitalize the names of languages or adjectives that describe the people from a certain country.**

Examples: Chinese   Spanish   Egyptians

Rule 2: **Always capitalize the names of books, magazines, newspapers, and other publications.**

Examples: *The Scarlet Letter*   *Catcher in the Rye*
                  Sports Illustrated

Remember that minor words like *of* or *the* are not capitalized when they are in the middle of a title.

Rule 3: **Always capitalize the first word in a sentence.**

Example: Who could love a crocodile?

Rule 4: **Always capitalize days of the week, months, and holidays.**

Examples: Thursday   August   Thanksgiving

Rule 5: **Always capitalize the names of people, titles, schools, and organizations.**

Examples: Professor John Young   University of Florida   Salvation Army

Rule 6: **Capitalize the names of geographical terms or places like cities, states, countries, rivers, mountains, etc.**

Examples: Louisiana   Germany   Potomac River
                 Rocky Mountains   Atlantic Ocean

Above is a Study List of words. The rules of capitalization apply to all of these words. It is also important to know the spelling of these words. Remember, if a word is supposed to be capitalized and it is not, it is considered to be misspelled.

SKILL DRILL 1

Rewrite each of the following words on the lines provided. Then circle the capital letters in each.

1. Germany _____
2. University of Florida _____
3. Thanksgiving_____
4. Thursday _____
5. *Sports Illustrated* _____
6. August _____
7. Chinese _____
8. Egyptians _____

9. New Year's Day _____
10. Spanish _____
11. Rocky Mountains _____
12. Mississippi River _____
13. *The Scarlet Letter* _____
14. *Catcher in the Rye* _____

15. Louisiana _____

SKILL DRILL 2

Answer the following questions by using words from the Study List.

Which word is the name of a state?   Which word is the name of a country?

1. _____   2. _____

Which words are the names of languages?

3. _____   4. _____

Which words are geographical locations?

5. _____   6. _____

Which words are the names of holidays?

7. _____   8. _____

Which words are the names of books or magazines?

9. _____   10. _____

11. _____

Which words are the names of days or months?

12. _____   13. _____

Which is the name of a school?   Which word is the name of a nationality?

14. _____   15. _____

▼

SKILL DRILL 3

In the following sentences, certain Study List words should be capitalized. Find those words and rewrite them, correctly capitalized, on the lines provided.

1. Today we will talk about the people and climate of germany.   _____

2. The egyptians often decorated crocodiles with gold.   _____

3. The meeting will be held on the third day in august.   _____

4. The mississippi river flows through the state of Louisiana.   _____

5. The thursday morning class will meet on Friday.   _____

6. Please read chapter two of *catcher in the rye*.   _____

7. Ed reads *sports illustrated* every week.   _____

8. How many people present have read *the scarlet letter*?   _____

9. Patricia will be attending the university of florida next year.   _____

10. This season we will be skiing in the rocky mountains.   _____

11. We always have turkey on thanksgiving.   _____

12. louisiana borders on the Gulf of Mexico.   _____

13. Many of our students speak spanish.   _____

14. The parade will be held on new year's day.   _____

15. Donna knows how to say ''thank you'' in chinese.   _____

▼

SKILL DRILL 4

Fill in the blanks in the following words to form words from the Study List. Then write the words you have formed on the lines provided. Be sure to capitalize where necessary.

1. sp _ rts
   _ ll _ str _ ted _____

2. ca _ _ _ er
   in the r _ e _____

3. th _ rsd _ y _____

4. mi_ _ i _ _ i _ _ i _____
   r_ _ _ _r

5. a _ g _ st _____

6. e _ _ pti _ ns _____

7. g _ rm _ ny _____

8. ch _ n _ s _ _____

9. new _ e _ r's day _____

10. sp _ n _ sh _____

11. l _ _ _ s _ _ na _____

12. th _ nk _ g _ v _ ng _____

13. rock _
m _ _ nt _ _ ns _____

14. un _ vers _ ty of
fl _ r _ da _____

15. *the s _ _ rl _ _*
letter   _____

WORD GAME 18

The words from the Study List are used in this puzzle. The numbers of the clues match the numbers of the puzzle. Read the clues below. Then write your answers in the puzzle blocks.

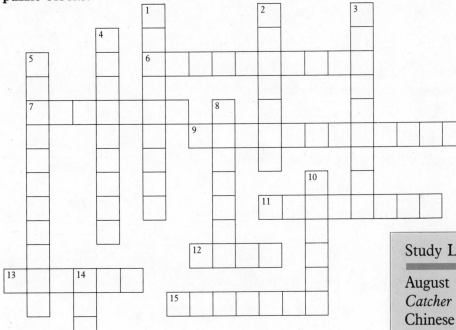

ACROSS
6. _____ of Florida
7. Language of Spain
9. November holiday
11. A day of the week
12. Happy New _____
13. _____ *Illustrated*
15. The_____ *Letter*

DOWN
1. _____ River
2. Rocky _____
3. State that begins with capital *L*
4. Country that begins with a capital *G*
5. People of Egypt
8. Language of China
10. Eighth month of the year
14. *Catcher in the* _____

Study List

August
Catcher in the Rye
Chinese
Egyptians
Germany
Louisiana
Mississippi River
New Year's Day
Rocky Mountains
Spanish
Sports Illustrated
Thanksgiving
The Scarlet Letter
Thursday
University of Florida

HOW WELL CAN YOU SPELL?

Try to take this practice test without looking back at Lesson 18. After you have finished, check your work against the Study List. Correct any mistakes you have made.

In each of the following sentences, one word is spelled incorrectly. Find that word. Then spell it correctly on the line provided. Remember that a word is misspelled if it is not capitalized when it should be.

1. The students at the university of florada have pet alligators.   _____

2. Please buy a copy of Hawthorne's *the scarlit letter*.   _____

3. This flight will travel over the rockie mountains.   _____

4. thankgiving is celebrated at the end of November.   _____

5. The swamps of louisiana are thick with gators.   _____

6. Next year we will learn how to speak spaniesh.   _____

7. January first is new yeer's day.   _____

8. That book has been translated from chinese into English.   _____

9. Many of those automobiles are made in germiny.   _____

10. The pyramids were built by the ancient egiptians.   _____

11. agust is the eighth month of the year.   _____

12. We will be riding the riverboat down the mississipi river.   _____

13. The party will be held on thersday of next week.   _____

14. The prize is a two-year subscription to *sport illestrated*.   _____

15. The book report on *cacher in the rye* is due tomorrow.   _____

Current Electricity

Think of a huge turbine engine that is larger than a sports arena. (A turbine engine is one that generates electricity.) At the center of the turbine are two large fans. Suppose that some of these turbines were sunk into the Gulf Stream off the Florida coast. The current of the stream turns the giant fans. The turbines convert the ocean's energy into electricity. The result is enough electric power to meet the needs of the State of Florida.

The plan may sound crazy. But it is one of more than 5,000 new energy ideas for the future. Scientists have fed all the information they know about the turbines into a computer. The computer gave the project a "yes" vote. But it will probably take 20 billion dollars to make the dream come true.

The turbines would be placed 25 miles off the coast of Florida. Two hundred and fifty of them would be anchored in the area called the Gulf Stream, which is the swiftest flowing ocean current in the world. Each machine would be 75 feet below the surface of the water. That would be deep enough so that ships in the vicinity could pass without any problem.

Scientists worry about the effect that the turbines would have on the Gulf Stream itself. The stream's current controls the weather pattern for much of the Atlantic Ocean. A change in this weather pattern might upset the environment.

In any case, scientists are looking for new ways to produce clean, cheap energy in large amounts. This must be done before our supply of oil and natural gas runs out. Ocean turbines may be one of the ways in which they will solve this problem.

REVIEWING YOUR READING

Circle the letter beside the word or phrase that best completes the sentence.

1. A turbine engine generates

    a. water.
    b. electricity.
    c. oil.
    d. natural gas.

2. The ocean turbines may be sunk in the

    a. Gulf Stream.
    b. Pacific Ocean.
    c. Indian Ocean.
    d. Boston Harbor.

3. The turbines would generate enough electricity to supply the needs of

    a. Georgia.
    b. Alabama.
    c. Texas.
    d. Florida.

4. The Gulf Stream's current is very

    a. fast.
    b. slow.
    c. warm.
    d. cold.

5. If the turbines are used, there will be

    a. 250 of them.
    b. 500 of them.
    c. 750 of them.
    d. 1000 of them.

6. The Gulf Stream's current controls the weather pattern for much of the

    a. northwest states.
    b. southwest states.
    c. Atlantic Ocean.
    d. Pacific Ocean.

7. According to the story, you can conclude that ocean turbines

    a. are being used today.
    b. have been used for many years.
    c. are an idea for the future.
    d. will never be used.

8. According to the story, you can conclude that the ocean turbines

    a. may be one idea to help solve our energy problems.
    b. definitely will not work.
    c. are the answer to all our energy problems.
    d. are guaranteed to work.

FIGURING THE FACTS

Decide whether the following statements are true or false. Write *T* on the line if the statement is true. If the statement is false, cross out the incorrect word or phrase in the sentence. Then write the correct word or phrase on the line to make the statement true.

1. At the center of the ocean there are six turbine fans. _____

2. The Gulf Stream is off the Florida coast. _____

3. The turbines will convert the ocean's energy to gasoline. _____

4. Scientists are studying more than 5,000 energy ideas. _____

5. The computer gave the turbine project a ''no'' vote. _____

6. The ocean turbine project will cost 100 billion dollars. _____

7. The turbines would be placed above the surface of the water. _____

8. The Gulf Stream controls the weather pattern for much of the Atlantic Ocean. _____

9. A change in the weather pattern could upset the environment. _____

10. Scientists have found many ways to produce clean, cheap energy. _____

WHAT'S YOUR OPINION?

1. Does the idea of ocean turbines sound farfetched to you? Why or why not?

_____

_____

_____

_____

2. Why do you think we need large amounts of clean, cheap energy?

_____

_____

_____

_____

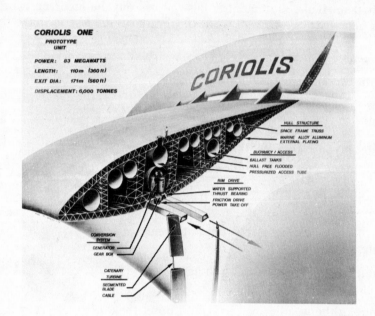

CORIOLIS ONE
PROTOTYPE
UNIT

POWER: 83 MEGAWATTS
LENGTH: 110m (360 ft)
EXIT DIA: 171m (560 ft)
DISPLACEMENT: 6,000 TONNES

DEVELOPING SPELLING SKILLS

Study List

campaign
guarantee
impossible
merchandise
occasion
parallel
previous
probably
responsibility
thoroughly
tomorrow
tremendous
unnecessary
unusual
vicinity

The following words appear in the reading selection.

tomorrow   probably   vicinity

Because these words are more tricky to spell than other words, we call them spelling demons. Experts have found that these are words people most often misspell. However, these demons are not really difficult to spell, if we remember what it is that makes each word tricky.

Examples: In the word *tomorrow*, there is a double *r* and a *w* at the end.

In *probably*, there are two *b's*.

In *vicinity*, the "viss" sound is spelled *vic*.

Of course, you may think there are other tricky letters in these words. The most important thing for you to do is make a note of what it is that makes the word difficult for you to spell.

On your left is a Study List of words. Each is considered a spelling demon. Keep in mind that these words are ones that you will use often in your writing. Study them extra carefully. Be sure to take notice of the letters in the word that make that word difficult for you to spell.

SKILL DRILL 1

Rewrite the following words on the lines provided. Then circle the letter or letters that make each word difficult to spell.

1. probably _____
2. responsibility _____
3. occasion _____
4. campaign _____
5. tomorrow _____
6. guarantee _____
7. merchandise _____

8. vicinity _____
9. previous _____
10. unusual _____
11. unnecessary _____
12. tremendous _____
13. impossible _____
14. parallel _____

15. thoroughly _____

SKILL DRILL 2

The following are short definitions of words from the Study List. Fill the blanks with words from the Study List that match the definitions. If you need help, check the Mini-Dictionary in the back of this book.

1. Goods for sale _____
2. At the same distance apart everywhere _____
3. More likely than not _____
4. Completely; totally _____
5. A region near or about a place _____
6. Duty; dependability _____
7. The day after today _____
8. A particular time or special event _____
9. Out of the ordinary; not usual _____
10. A planned course of action for a special purpose (like an election) _____
11. Not needed; not absolutely necessary _____
12. Coming or going before; earlier _____
13. Very great; enormous _____
14. A promise to pay or do something if another fails _____
15. That which cannot be done _____

SKILL DRILL 3

Fill the blanks in each of the following words to form words from the Study List. Then write the word you have formed on the line provided.

1. un _ _ c _ _ _ ary _____

2. un _ _ _ _ l _____

3. tom _ _ _ ow _____

4. g _ _ r _ nt _ _ _____

5. par _ _ _ el _____

6. pro _ a _ _ _ _____

7. v _ _ _ nity _____

8. pre _ _ _ us _____

9. cam _ _ _ gn _____

10. tr _ men _ _ _ s _____

11. im _ _ _ _ _ ble _____

12. merch _ _ di _ _ _____

13. th _ r _ ugh _ _ _____

14. re _ _ on _ _ bility _____

15. o _ _ as _ _ n _____

SKILL DRILL 4

Answer the following questions by using words from the Study List.

Which words end with the suffix *ty*?

1. _____   2. _____

Which words end with the suffix *ous*?

3. _____   4. _____

Which word contains the word *rough*?

5. _____

Which words contain the letter combination *ss*?

6. _____   7. _____

Which word contains the letter combination *cc*?

8. _____

Which word contains the word *camp*?

9. _____

Which word contains the word *usual*?

10. _____

Which word contains the letter combination *ll*?

11. _____

Which word contains the prefix *pro*?

12. _____

Which word contains the word *tee*?

13. _____

Which word contains the letter combination *ise*?

14. _____

Which word contains the letter combination *rr*?

15. _____

WORD GAME 19

All of the letters from the words in the Study List appear in this puzzle. Cross out the letters of the puzzle as you use them to spell the Study List words. There will be enough letters left to answer the question below.

```
                      A
                   A  A  A
                A  A  A  A  A
             A  A  B  B  B  B  C
          C  C  C  C  C  D  D  E  E
       E  E  E  E  E  E  E  E  E  E  E
       E  G  G  G  G  H  H  H  I  I  I  I  I
    I  I  I  I  I  I  I  L  L  L  L  L  L  L  L
 M  M  M  M  M  N  N  N  N  N  N  N  N  N  N  O
    O  O  O  O  O  O  O  O  O  O  P  P  P  P
       P  P  R  R  R  R  R  R  R  R  R  R
          R  S  S  S  S  S  S  S  S  S
             S  T  T  T  T  T  U  U
                U  U  U  U  U  V
                   V  W  Y  Y  Y
                      Y  Y  Y
```

Study List

campaign
guarantee
impossible
merchandise
occasion
parallel
previous
probably
responsibility
thoroughly
tomorrow
tremendous
unnecessary
unusual
vicinity

What are scientists looking for? _____

HOW WELL CAN YOU SPELL?

Try to take this practice test without looking back at Lesson 19. After you have finished, check your work against the Study List. Correct any mistakes you have made.

A. One word in each of the following pairs of words is spelled incorrectly. Circle that word and spell it correctly on the line provided.

1. visinity, responsibility   _____

2. tremendus, previous   _____

3. impossible, throughly   _____

4. campaign, unnecesary   _____

5. unusual, occassion   _____

6. parrallel, merchandise   _____

7. probally, tomorrow   _____

8. thoroughly, garuntee   _____

B. In each of the following sentences, one word is spelled incorrectly. Find that word. Then spell it correctly on the line provided.

9. This puzzle seems almost imposible to do.   _____

10. This campane is the most exciting one I have seen.   _____

11. That was a most unuseual movie.   _____

12. All of the merchandice on that table is for sale.   _____

13. The test will be held the day after tomorow.   _____

14. Having a family is a huge responsability.   _____

15. The answer may be found in the preveus chapter.   _____

The Haunted Jewel

For over three hundred years, the mysterious Hope Diamond has been the subject of rumor and superstition. The blue stone is one of the largest, most beautiful diamonds in the world. Legend has it that it holds the curse of a Hindu goddess.

The tale of the stone begins in India, where it once adorned the statue of a goddess. When the gem was stolen, the goddess became angry. She cursed the thieves and anyone who chose to possess the glittering jewel.

Years later in the 1700s, the gem found its way into the hands of the French queen, Marie Antoinette. But she did not own the stone for very long. The curse plainly had its effect on Marie Antoinette, for she was beheaded during the French Revolution. Thieves then made off with the diamond, which the French people had named "the French Blue."

In 1830, the stone reappeared in London. A banker named Henry Hope purchased it for $90,000.00. Although Mr. Hope gave the diamond his name, the curse still seemed to be working. Henry Hope died penniless. But the diamond moved on to new owners. A European prince bought it for an actress and later shot her. A Greek owner died with his family when his automobile went over a cliff. And a Turkish sultan who owned the stone was overthrown by his army.

The Hope's first American owner was Evelyn Walsh McLean. She had seen the diamond when it belonged to the sultan and wished to have it. She paid twice what the stone cost Mr. Hope—$180,000.00. Not fearing the curse, Mrs. McLean had the stone set into a necklace. She wore it often and with great pride. Both of her children died tragic deaths. Her husband died of mental illness.

Is it a curse or a coincidence? That depends on what you choose to believe. After Mrs. McLean's death, the stone was donated to the Smithsonian Institution in Washington, D.C. The Museum has owned the steel-blue diamond for over 30 years. No disasters have happened—yet!

REVIEWING YOUR READING

Circle the letter beside the word or phrase that best completes the sentence.

1. The tale of the Hope Diamond begins in

   a. France.
   b. London.
   c. India.
   d. America.

2. The gem once *adorned* a religious statue. The word *adorned* means

   a. decorated.
   b. polished.
   c. held up.
   d. worshiped.

3. The stone's curse was brought about by

   a. a French queen.
   b. an American millionaire.
   c. a European prince.
   d. a Hindu goddess.

4. Marie Antoinette died during the

   a. American Revolution.
   b. French Revolution.
   c. French and Indian War.
   d. Second World War.

5. The famous stone was once called the

   a. McLean Gold.
   b. French Blue.
   c. Greek Green.
   d. French White.

6. Mr. Henry Hope was a

   a. comedian.
   b. sultan.
   c. king.
   d. banker.

7. In order to buy the diamond, Mrs. McLean paid

   a. the same price as Mr. Hope.
   b. twice what Mr. Hope had paid.
   c. less than what Mr. Hope had paid.
   d. three times what Mr. Hope had paid.

8. The stone is presently in

   a. a French Museum.
   b. Mr. Hope's collection.
   c. the Smithsonian Institution.
   d. the Metropolitan Museum.

FIGURING THE FACTS

Decide whether the following statements are true or false. Write *T* on the line if the statement is true. If the statement is false, cross out the incorrect word or phrase in the sentence. Then write the correct word or phrase on the line to make the statement true.

1. There have been rumors about the Hope Diamond for 300 years. _____

2. The diamond is green in color. _____

3. Marie Antoinette was hanged during the French Revolution. _____

4. Henry Hope purchased the diamond for $90,000. _____

5. When Henry Hope died, he was very rich. _____

6. A prince once bought the diamond for a South American singer. _____

7. The stone was once owned by a Turkish sultan. _____

8. Evelyn Walsh McLean was the Hope's second American owner. _____

9. Mrs. McLean had the stone set into a crown. _____

10. Mrs. McLean's husband died of mental illness. _____

WHAT'S YOUR OPINION?

1. Do you believe that the diamond is cursed? Why or why not?

_____
_____
_____
_____

2. Why do you think Mrs. McLean purchased the Hope Diamond even after tragic deaths had come to all its previous owners?

_____
_____
_____
_____

DEVELOPING SPELLING SKILLS

Study List

diamond
interpret
loneliness
medicine
possess
preferred
proceed
punctuation
recommend
rumor
separate
statue
straighten
succeed
vitamin

The following words appear in the reading selection.

diamond   rumor   possess   statue

When learning the words in this chapter, it is most important that you make a mental note of what it is in each word that makes it difficult for you to spell.

Examples: In the word *diamond*, the letter *a* is easy to forget because it isn't sounded.

In *rumor*, the *o* is often confused with *e*.

In *possess*, there are two sets of double *s*.

In *statue*, the *e* is silent.

On your left is a Study List of words. Each is considered a spelling demon. Take extra care when studying these words. Notice what it is in each word that makes the word difficult or confusing.

SKILL DRILL 1

Rewrite the following words on the lines provided. Then circle the letter or letters that make each word difficult to spell.

1. separate _____
2. succeed _____
3. loneliness _____
4. punctuation _____
5. recommend _____
6. vitamin _____
7. preferred _____

8. straighten _____
9. diamond _____
10. possess _____
11. rumor _____
12. statue _____
13. interpret _____
14. medicine _____

15. proceed _____

SKILL DRILL 2

The following are short definitions of words from the Study List. Fill the blanks with words from the Study List that match the definitions. If you need help, check the Mini-Dictionary in the back of this book.

1. A story or statement lacking in proof or truth _____

2. An image carved in stone, wood, etc. _____

3. To explain the meaning of _____

4. A substance used to cure disease _____

5. To keep apart; divide _____

6. To turn out well; to have success _____

7. A precious stone _____

8. The state of feeling or being alone _____

9. To own or to have _____

10. The use of certain marks in written language to make the meaning clear _____

11. To speak in favor of or advise _____

12. Special substance needed for the nourishment of the body _____

13. Liked something better _____

14. To move forward _____

15. To make straight _____

SKILL DRILL 3

Fill the blanks in each of the following words to form words from the Study List. Then write the word you have formed on the line provided.

1. sep _ r _ te _____
2. rec _ _ _ end _____
3. inter _ _ et _____
4. d _ _ mo _ _ _____
5. pre _ _ _ _ ed _____
6. lon _ _ _ ness _____
7. r _ m _ r _____

8. su _ _ _ _ d _____
9. st _ t _ _ _____
10. med _ _ _ ne _____
11. v _ ta _ _ _ _____
12. pro _ _ _ d _____
13. str _ _ gh _ _ n _____
14. po _ _ e _ _ _____

15. pu _ _ _ uat _ _ n _____

SKILL DRILL 4

Answer the following questions by using words from the Study List.

Which word contains the consonant combination *ct*?

1. _____

Which words contain the suffix *ceed*?

2. _____   3. _____

Which word contains the word *mend*?

4. _____

Which word contains the word *rate*?

5. _____

Which word begins with the prefix *inter*?

6. _____

Which word has the vowel combination *ue*?

7. _____

Which word contains two sets of *ss*?

8. _____

Which word ends with the suffix *ness*?

9. _____

Which word ends with the suffix *or*?

10. _____

Which word contains the letter combination *rr*?

11. _____

Which word contains the vowel combination *ia*?

12. _____

Which word ends with *cine*?

13. _____

Which word begins with *vita*?

14. _____

Which word contains the word *straight*?

15. _____

Study List

diamond
interpret
loneliness
medicine
possess
preferred
proceed
punctuation
recommend
rumor
separate
statue
straighten
succeed
vitamin

WORD GAME 20

This is a crossword without clues! Study the length and spelling of each word in the Study List. Then figure out which words fit in the spaces.

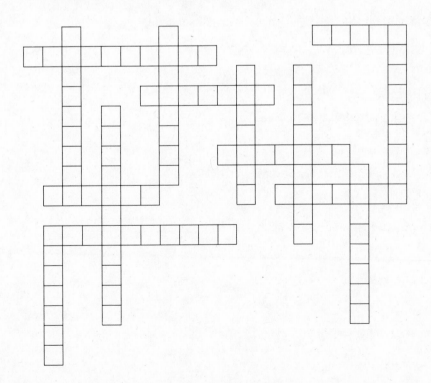

HOW WELL CAN YOU SPELL?

Try to take this practice test without looking back at Lesson 20. After you have finished, check your work against the Study List. Correct any mistakes you have made.

A. One word in each of the following pairs of words is spelled incorrectly. Circle that word and spell it correctly on the line provided.

1. recomend, rumor   _____

2. diamond, interpet   _____

3. stachew, medicine   _____

4. posess, proceed   _____

5. succeed, lonliness   _____

6. straiten, vitamin   _____

7. preferred, seperate   _____

8. punctuashun, statue   _____

B. In each of the following sentences, one word is spelled incorrectly. Find that word. Then spell it correctly on the line provided.

9. The parade will procede down Fifth Avenue.   _____

10. I have always prefered classical music to rock.   _____

11. Vitamen A is most important to good health.   _____

12. Whatever you choose to do, I know you will succede.   _____

13. Don't forget to take your medecine before you go to sleep.   _____

14. That dimond is very expensive.   _____

15. Don't pay any attention to that rumer.   _____

MINI-DICTIONARY

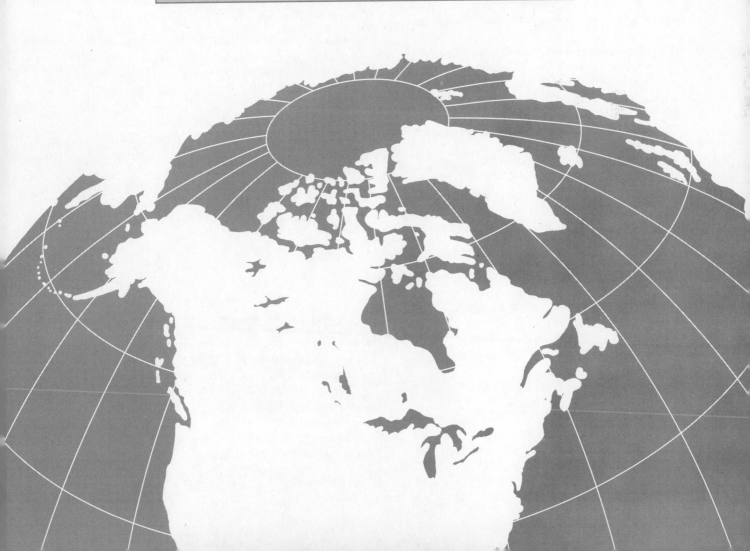

A

absence *[AB suns]* the state of being away

absolutely *[ab suh LOOT lee]* without any restrictions; completely

accept *[ak SEPT]* to take or receive

acceptance *[ak SEP tuns]* the act of taking something offered or given

accidentally *[ak sih DEN tuh lee]* mistakenly; unexpectedly

accomplice *[uh KOM plis]* a person who aids another in committing a crime

accurately *[AK yur it lee]* correctly

acquaintance *[uh KWAYN tuns]* a person you know but not as a close friend

actually *[AK choo uh lee]* really or in fact

advance *[ad VANS]* to move forward

adventure *[ad VEN chur]* an unusual or exciting experience
Plural: **adventures** *[ad VEN churz]*

advertise *[AD vur tyz]* to give public notice in a newspaper or on TV, etc.

advice *[ad VYS]* helpful suggestions

advise *[ad VYZ]* to give advice

allowance *[uh LOU uns]* a limited share of money or goods that is allowed to be given

alloys *[AL oiz]* metals made by mixing two or more metals

ambitious *[am BISH us]* showing a strong desire for fame or honor

ambulance *[AM byuh luns]* a vehicle used to carry sick people
Plural: **ambulances** *[AM byuh luns ez]*

annoyance *[uh NOI uns]* something that bothers or disturbs you

apology *[uh POL uh jee]* words of pardon for an offense or accident
Plural: **apologies** *[uh POL uh jeez]*

appearance *[uh PEER uns]* the act of coming in sight or appearing

apprentice *[uh PREN tis]* a person learning a trade or art

approach *[uh PROHCH]* to come near or nearer something

artist *[AR tist]* a person who paints pictures

assistance *[uh SIS tuns]* help or aid

associate *[uh SOH see ayt]* to join or connect with something

attract *[uh TRAKT]* to draw something or someone to oneself

audience *[AW dee uns]* people gathered in a place to hear or see something

August *[AW gust]* the eighth month of the year

authority *[uh THOR ih tee]* officials of the government
Plural: **authorities** *[uh THOR ih teez]*

autobiography *[AW tuh by OG ruh fee]* the story of a person's life written by him- or herself

avoid *[uh VOID]* to keep away from

B

banjo *[BAN joh]* a hand-held, stringed musical instrument
Plural: **banjos** *[BAN johz]*

betrayed *[bih TRAYD]* was unfaithful to something or gave away a secret

biscuit *[BIS kit]* a small, soft breadlike cake

bouquet *[boh KAY]* a bunch of flowers

budget *[BUJ it]* a plan for spending time or money
Plural: **budgets** *[BUJ its]*

buffalo *[BUF uh loh]* a large, shaggy animal with stong legs; a bison
Plural: **buffaloes** *[BUF uh lohs]*

bush *[BOOSH]* a woody plant that is smaller than a tree
Plural: **bushes** *[BOOSH is]*

C

calf *[KAF]* a young cow, bull, whale, or elephant
Plural: **calves** *[KAVZ]*

campaign *[kam PAYN]* a planned course of action for a special purpose (such as an election)

career *[kuh REER]* a job or course of progress through life

caution *[KAW shun]* to warn or advise

ceiling *[SEE ling]* the inside top covering of a room

certainly *[SUR tun lee]* without any doubt or question

characteristic *[KAR ik tuh RIS tik]* a quality that shows how a person or thing is different from others
Plural: **characteristics** *[KAR ik tuh RIS tiks]*

cheerfully *[CHEER ful ee]* done with joy or gladness

cheese *[CHEEZ]* a solid food made from milk
Plural: **cheeses** *[CHEEZ is]*

circumference *[sur KUM fur uns]* the boundary line of a circle

class *[KLAS]* a meeting of a group of students and a teacher
Plural: **classes** *[KLAS is]*

classified *[KLAS uh fyd]* arranged in classes or groups

clearance *[KLEER uns]* the act of clearing a space

cleverly *[KLEV ur lee]* quick in thinking; smart

closet *[KLOZ it]* a small room used to store clothing
Plural: **closets** *[KLOZ its]*

clumsily *[KLUM zuh lee]* in an awkward manner

coarsely *[KOHRS lee]* roughly; harshly

coincidence *[koh IN sih duns]* a chance meeting that is remarkable

commence *[kuh MENS]* to start or begin something

committee *[kuh MIT ee]* a group of persons appointed to do certain things

compact *[kum PAKT]* firmly packed together; small

complement *[KOM pluh ment]* that which completes or makes perfect

compliment *[KOM pluh ment]* something said in praise of someone

confidence *[KON fih duns]* a firm belief in oneself

construct *[kun STRUKT]* to put together or build

convenience *[kun VEEN yuns]* quality of being convenient or handy

conveying *[kun VAY ing]* transporting or carrying something

cooperate *[koh OP uh rayt]* to unite and work together

copied *[KOP eed]* having made a copy of something

correspondence *[kawr ih SPON duns]* an exchange of letters; letter writing

couldn't *[KOOD unt]* could not

council *[KOUN sul]* a group of people called together to talk things over

counsel *[KOUN sul]* to give advice

counterfeit *[KOUN tur fit]* not real; an illegal copy

criticize *[KRIT ih syz]* to find fault with something

crutches *[KRUCH is]* supports to help a lame person walk

D

decayed *[dih KAYD]* rotted; losing strength or beauty

decoy *[dih KOI]* something used to lure or tempt someone into danger
Plural: **decoys** *[dih KOIS]*

defying *[dih FY ing]* resisting or challenging authority

desperately *[DES pur it lee]* reckless because one has lost hope

destroyed *[dih STROID]* broken into pieces; ended

diamond *[DY mund]* a precious stone

difference *[DIF ur uns]* the condition of being different; unlikeness

disguise *[dis GYZ]* a change in appearance to look like someone else

disobeyed *[dis uh BAYD]* refused or failed to obey

displaying *[dis PLAY ing]* showing or exposing to view

distance *[DIS tuns]* the space between two things, places, or people

distract *[dih STRAKT]* to draw away, confuse, or disturb

doesn't *[DUZ unt]* does not

E

elf *[ELF]* a tiny, mischievous character in fairy tales
Plural: **elves** *[ELVZ]*

emergency *[ih MUR jun see]* a sudden need for immediate action
Plural: **emergencies** *[ih MUR jun sees]*

employer *[em PLOI ur]* a person or firm that hires someone to work endurance *[en DOOR uns]* power to keep on or last

entirely *[en TYUR lee]* including all the parts

entrance *[EN truns]* the place through which to enter

envying *[EN vee ing]* being jealous of another's good fortune

essential *[uh SEN shul]* necessary; needed to make a thing what it is

except *[ik SEPT]* but

exercise *[EK sur syz]* activity that improves the body

existence *[ig ZIS tuns]* life; the state of being

experience *[ik SPEER ee uns]* everything you have ever felt or done, or what has happened to you

---

F

faithfully *[FAYTH ful lee]* loyally; honestly

February *[FEB roo er ee]* the second month of the year

finally *[FYN uh lee]* last; coming at the end

finance *[fy NANS]* money matters
Plural: finances *[fy NANS is]*

flair *[FLAIR]* a natural talent

flare *[FLAIR]* a dazzling burst of flame or light

fox *[FOKS]* a wild animal that is sly and crafty
Plural: foxes *[FOKS is]*

G

gracefully *[GRAYS ful lee]* beautifully and smoothly

guarantee *[gar un TEE]* a promise to pay or do something if another fails

guessing *[GES ing]* forming an opinion without really knowing

---

H

half *[HAF]* one of two equal parts
Plural: halves *[HAVZ]*

hatchet *[HACH it]* a small axe that is used with one hand
Plural: hatchets *[HACH its]*

haven't *[HAV unt]* have not

hero *[HEER oh]* a person admired for bravery or great deeds
Plural: heroes *[HEER ohs]*

hoof *[HOOF]* a hard covering on the feet of some animals
Plural: hooves *[HOOVZ]*

I

ignorance *[IG nur uns]* a lack of knowledge

immediately *[ih MEE dee it lee]* without delay; happening at once

impact *[IM pakt]* collision; the striking of one thing against another

importance *[im POR tuns]* the quality of being important

impossible *[im POS uh bul]* that which cannot be done

improvise *[IM pruh vyz]* to make something up as you go along

inch *[INCH]* a measure of length
Plural: inches *[INCH is]*

independence *[in dih PEN duns]* freedom from control or help of another

individual *[in duh VIJ oo ul]* one single person

influence *[IN floo uns]* to have power over another

initially *[ih NISH uh lee]* first; coming at the beginning

injury *[IN juh ree]* damage from harm or hurts
Plural: injuries *[IN juh rees]*

inspector *[in SPEK tur]* a person who inspects or looks over carefully

insurance *[in SHOOR uns]* insuring of life, person, or property against loss

interpret *[in TUR prit]* to explain the meaning of

itemize *[EYE tuh myz]* to list by items

it's *[ITS]* it is

J

journey *[JUR nee]* a long trip or travel
Plural: journeys *[JUR neez]*

June *[JOON]* the sixth month of the year

K

knife *[NYF]* a cutting tool with a sharp edge
Plural: knives *[NYVZ]*
knowledge *[NOL ij]* what one knows

L

language *[LAN gwij]* human speech; spoken or written
leaf *[LEEF]* a thin, green part of a tree or plant
Plural: leaves *[LEEVZ]*
legally *[LEE gul lee]* allowed by law; lawfully
lieutenant *[loo TEN unt]* an army officer
life *[LYF]* the period of living
Plural: lives *[LYVZ]*
loaf *[LOHF]* bread shaped in one long piece
Plural: loaves *[LOHVZ]*
locally *[LOH kuh lee]* within a particular place; nearby
loneliness *[LOHN lee ness]* the state of feeling or being alone
luckily *[LUK uh lee]* having a good result by chance

M

magazine *[mag uh ZEEN]* a regular publication containing stories and articles
Plural: magazines *[mag uh ZEENZ]*
magnifying *[MAG nuh fy ing]* making something look bigger than it really is
managed *[MAN ijd]* controlled or handled
manual *[MAN yoo ul]* done with the hands
mechanic *[muh KAN ik]* a person who works on machines
medicine *[MED ih sin]* a substance used to cure disease
merchandise *[MUR chun dyz]* goods for sale
mileage *[MY lij]* miles covered or traveled
morning *[MORN ing]* the early part of the day
mourning *[MORN ing]* showing sorrow for someone's death

multiplying *[MUL tuh ply ing]* increasing in number or amount

N

naturally *[NACH ur uh lee]* in a natural way; as one might expect
nearly *[NEER lee]* almost; not quite
nervous *[NUR vus]* restless or uneasy

O

occasion *[uh KAY zhun]* a particular time or special event
occasionally *[uh KAY zhuh nul ee]* once in a while; now and then
occupied *[OK yuh pyd]* taken up, filled, or lived in
opinion *[uh PIN yun]* what a person thinks
Plural: opinions *[uh PIN yuns]*
optional *[OP shuh nul]* not required; left to one's own choice
ourself *[our SELF]* we or us
Plural: ourselves *[our SELVZ]*

P

parade *[puh RAYD]* a march or display
Plural: parades *[puh RAYDZ]*
parallel *[PAR uh lel]* at the same distance apart everywhere
passenger *[PAS un jur]* a person who rides on some means of transportation
patronize *[PAY truh nyz]* to be a regular customer of something
performance *[pur FOR muns]* the acting of a show, movie, etc.
piano *[pee AN oh]* a large musical instrument played by striking the keys on its keyboard
Plural: pianos *[pe AN ohz]*
portfolio *[pohrt FOH lee oh]* portable case for papers; a briefcase
Plural: portfolios *[pohrt FOH lee ohs]*

possess *[puh ZES]* to own or to have
potato *[puh TAY toh]* a white vegetable
    Plural: **potatoes** *[puh TAY tohs]*
pouch *[POUCH]* a bag or sack
    Plural: **pouches** *[POUCH ez]*
practically *[PRAK tih kul ee]* almost or nearly
practice *[PRAK tis]* action done over and over for skill
preferred *[prih FURD]* liked something better
prejudice *[PREJ uh dis]* an opinion formed without judging fairly
presence *[PREZ uns]* the state of being present
previous *[PREE vee us]* coming or going before; earlier
privilege *[PRIV uh lij]* a special right or advantage
probably *[PROB uh blee]* more likely than not
proceed *[pruh SEED]* to move forward
proclaim *[proh KLAYM]* to declare or make known publicly
punctuation *[pungk choo AY shun]* the use of certain marks in written language to make the meaning clear
pursuit *[pur SOOT]* the act of pursuing or following

R

radio *[RAY dee oh]* a way of sending or receiving sounds by electric waves
    Plural: **radios** *[RAY dee ohs]*
radish *[RAD ish]* a small, crisp red vegetable
    Plural: **radishes** *[RAD ish es]*
rapidly *[RAP id lee]* very swiftly or quickly
realize *[REE uh lyz]* to understand clearly
really *[REE uh lee]* truly or actually
recently *[REE sunt lee]* happening a short time ago
recommend *[rek uh MEND]* to speak in favor of or advise
recruit *[rih KROOT]* to get new members
reference *[REF ur uns]* the act of referring or consulting
reflex *[REE fleks]* an automatic response
    Plural: **reflexes** *[REE fleks ez]*

relaying *[REE lay ing]* taking something and carrying it farther
reliable *[rih LY uh bul]* dependable; worthy of trust
relying *[rih LY ing]* depending on or trusting
remembrance *[rih MEM bruns]* the act of remembering
respectfully *[rih SPEKT ful ee]* feeling or showing respect
responsibility *[rih spon suh BIL ih tee]* duty; dependability
revise *[rih VYZ]* to make corrections or improvements
ring *[RING]* to make a clear sound by touching or striking
rodeo *[ROH dee oh]* a contest in riding horses or roping cattle
    Plural: **rodeos** *[ROH dee ohs]*
rumor *[ROO mur]* a story or statement lacking in proof or truth

---
S

salvage *[SAL vij]* to rescue or save from being thrown away
sandwich *[SAND wich]* two slices of bread with filling between such as meat or cheese
    Plural: **sandwiches** *[SAND wich es]*
satisfied *[SAT is fyd]* contented or fulfilled
scene *[SEEN]* the time or place of a play, story, or happening
schedule *[SKE jool]* written or printed statement of details
    Plural: **schedules** *[SKE jools]*
sealing *[SEEL ing]* closing tightly
secretary *[SEK rih ter ee]* skilled office worker
seen *[SEEN]* having looked at
separate *[SEP uh rayt]* to keep apart; divide
separately *[SEP ur it lee]* divided into parts or groups; individually
September *[sep TEM bur]* the ninth month of the year
serious *[SEER ee us]* important; grave

shampoo *[sham POO]* a soap used to wash hair
    Plural: **shampoos** *[sham POOZ]*
shelf *[SHELF]* a piece of wood that is fastened to a
    wall to hold things such as books
    Plural: **shelves** *[SHELVZ]*
sheriff *[SHER if]* a law enforcement officer
    Plural: **sheriffs** *[SHER ifs]*
shouldn't *[SHOOD unt]* should not
sketch *[SKECH]* a rough or quickly done drawing
    Plural: **sketches** *[SKECH es]*
soprano *[suh PRAN oh]* a singer with the highest
    singing voice there is
    Plural: **sopranos** *[suh PRAN ohs]*
spectator *[SPEK tay tur]* a person who watches an
    event
    Plural: **spectators** *[SPEK tay turz]*
speeches *[SPEECH es]* public talks
splice *[SPLYS]* to join together
standardize *[STAN dur dyz]* to make standard in
    size, weight, shape, etc.
statue *[STACH oo]* an image carved in stone, wood,
    etc.
stereo *[STER ee oh]* a record player or radio that
    brings sound from two directions
    Plural: **stereos** *[STER ee ohs]*
stitch *[STICH]* a loop of thread made while sewing
    Plural: **stitches** *[STICH es]*
straighten *[STRAYT un]* to make straight
strayed *[STRAYD]* wandered or roamed away
studio *[STOO dee oh]* a workroom for a painter or
    other artist
    Plural: **studios** *[STOO dee ohs]*
study *[STUD ee]* a lesson or school subject
    Plural: **studies** *[STUD eez]*
succeed *[suk SEED]* to turn out well; to have
    success
summarize *[SUM uh ryz]* to make a summary of
superior *[suh PEER ee ur]* very good or above
    average
supplied *[suh PLYD]* having satisfied a need or
    provided a quantity of something
surveying *[sur VAY ing]* looking over or viewing
    something; skimming
swaying *[SWAY ing]* swinging back and forth

T

theater *[THEE uh tur]* a place where plays are acted
theory *[THI o ree]* explantion of why or how
    something happens
    Plural: **theories** *[THI o reez]*
thief *[THEEF]* one who steals
thoroughly *[THUR oh lee]* completely; totally
Thursday *[THURZ dee]* the fifth day of the week
tomato *[tuh MAY toh]* a juicy red vegetable
    Plural: **tomatoes** *[tuh MAY tohs]*
tomorrow *[tuh MOR oh]* the day after today
tornado *[tor NAY doh]* a violent and destructive
    storm; a whirlwind
    Plural: **tornadoes** *[tor NAY dohs]*
totally *[TOHT uh lee]* completely; entirely; in a total
    manner
tremendous *[trih MEN dus]* very great; enormous
trophy *[TROH fee]* a prize for the winner of a
    contest
    Plural: **trophies** *[TROH feez]*
Tuesday *[TOOZ dee]* the third day of the week

U

understood *[un dur STOOD]* to have learned the
    meaning of something
unnecessary *[un NES ih ser ee]* not needed; not
    absolutely necessary
unusual *[un YOO zhoo ul]* out of the ordinary; not
    usual

V

vacuum *[VAK yoo um]* an empty space without any
    air in it
valley *[VAL ee]* low land between hills or mountains
    Plural: **valleys** *[VAL leez]*
valuable *[VAL yoo uh bul]* having value
vegetable *[VEJ tuh bul]* a plant used for food
vicinity *[vih SIN ih tee]* a region near or about a
    place

vitamin *[VY tuh min]* special substances needed for the nourishment of the body
volcano *[vol KAY noh]* a mountain that expels steam and lava
    Plural: **volcanoes** *[vol KAY nohz]*

wearily *[WEER uh lee]* in a tired or worn-out way
Wednesday *[WENZ dee]* the fourth day of the week
we'll *[WEEL]* we will
wharf *[HWORF]* a platform for loading and unloading ships
    Plural: **wharves** *[HWORVZ]*
where's *[HWAIRZ]* where is
wife *[WYF]* a married woman
    Plural: **wives** *[WYFZ]*

wish *[WISH]* an expression of a desire or want
    Plural: **wishes** *[WISH es]*
wolf *[WOOLF]* a wild animal somewhat like a dog
    Plural: **wolves** *[WOOLVZ]*
woman *[WOOM un]* an adult female human
    Plural: **women** *[WIM in]*
won't *[WOHNT]* will not
wouldn't *[WOOD unt]* would not
wrap *[RAP]* to cover with paper and string
wreckage *[REK ij]* the remains of something ruined
wring *[RING]* to squeeze or twist

yourself *[yoor SELF]* you
    Plural: **yourselves** *[yoor SELVZ]*
you've *[YOOV]* you have